ABOUT THE AUTHOR

Wendy Lewis was born in West Sussex and grew up enjoying the freedom of the countryside, and the neighbouring farm. Educated at Chichester High School for girls, she went on to a varied career as a Post Office Clerk, Pub Landlady, Dog Breeder, Farmer, Freelance Journalist and mildly successful poet.

She has had many magazine articles published, and five short stories read on local radio.

The Reluctant Farmer is her first book.

GW00673152

THE RELUCTANT FARMER

THE RELUCTANT FARMER

by

WENDY LEWIS

MAZARD
West Sussex

Paperback ISBN 978-0-9545022-0-1

Published
by
Mazard
5 Heathfield Gardens
Midhurst
West Sussex
GU29 9HG

First published by Central Publishing Ltd. 2001
ISBN 1-903970-09-1

The Reluctant Farmer

We first saw Warren Hanger Farm on a cold January day, after a freezing night which had turned the ground to iron and silenced the birds.

Travelling along the single track 'with passing places' lane in Sussex we nearly missed the sign directing us to the farm. Overgrown by a straggly hedge and some dead stinging nettles it hung from the post by one remaining nail, and it pointed straight down.

This wasn't so far from the truth as we found when we turned onto the rough track, rattled over a cattle grid and bumped down the steep, slippery hillside. Fields on either side of the track fell away to a hedge and bank on one side, and woodland on the other.

The farmhouse, built of stone and tile-hung from the roof to just above the ground floor windows, was perched halfway down this hill and overlooked a valley of small fields interspersed with patches of woodland. Most of the farm buildings appeared to be at the bottom of the hill, about quarter of a mile away from the house. Not a very practical arrangement, I thought, but kept this to myself, not wanting to spoil Gerald's excitement.

Across a field from the house was a picturesque cottage with a neat garden. This was the only other dwelling within sight and behind it stretched acres of woodland rising to the heath beyond.

A rocky stream flowed out of these woods and tumbled through the farm fields, held up on its journey by stone troughs which provided water for the livestock, mostly wild-eyed sheep and lambs which scattered at the car's approach as we drove slowly down the muddy track and drew up in the farm yard.

Gerald turned off the engine and opened his door, letting in a blast of freezing air; it was a lot colder here than the London we had left earlier in the morning.

As he started to get out of the car a mean-looking, wall-eyed collie dog shot out from nowhere and grabbed his trouser leg.

"Bloody hell!" he shouted, withdrawing his leg and slamming the car door. "You understand dogs, get out and explain to it that we are friendly - and see if you can find someone to tie it up."

His reasoning that I understood dogs was based on the fact that I had brought three small dachshunds from my previous marriage into this one.

"Thanks very much," I said, trying to see where the collie had gone and unwilling to put my legendary power over dogs to the test.

My honour was saved by an elderly, wizened creature who appeared from behind a barn and dispatched the collie with an ancient Sussex curse.

"Mr Challen?" Gerald asked, glancing at notes he had made on the sale particulars.

"That's right. You would be Mr and Mrs Collins? Come in, come in."

We followed our rescuer through a rickety wooden gate which was precariously linked to the stone wall by a piece of rope and an old leather strap. The tiny walled garden between the yard and the farmhouse contained dead stinging nettles, a rusty refrigerator, a three-legged chair and some unidentifiable farm machinery. Against the house, beside the door, was a large slate trough holding two pots of dried compost, concreted to the roots of long-dead geraniums.

Mr Challen pushed open the half-glazed back door

which had once been painted scarlet, but was now well-weathered to a dull pink, and led us into a filthy scullery.

The floor appeared to be of stone but it was difficult to tell through the layer of cow dung encrusted straw, blue plastic fertilizer bags and ancient sacks.

I tried to catch Gerald's eye but he was busy talking to the old man.

What were we doing here? This wasn't anything like the cosy cottage I had imagined when he had first suggested a move to the country.

Tattered coats hung from nails banged into the wall, and below these lay two pairs of shapeless boots, well frayed around the tops from the enthusiastic attentions of the collie's teeth. This room probably doubled as a kennel when the dog wasn't out terrorising the neighbourhood.

The scullery led into the kitchen which, apart from being painted in primary reds, blues and yellows, had not altered since the place was built three hundred years ago. There were still hooks in the beam across the middle of the room from which, Mr Challen told us, his father had hung the butchered pigs while he quartered them ready for salting down in the old slate trough we had seen outside the back door.

"This has tremendous possibilities," said Gerald encouragingly to me.

"Yes," I said, distracted by Mr Challen who had just began to instruct me in the operation of the ancient solid fuel cooking range.

"You riddles it like this," he said, pulling a metal rod backwards and forwards and covering us and the kitchen in a fine layer of grey ash.

"Look, it's even got a bread oven," said Gerald,

unlatching the little iron door in the wall beside the range.

"Hasn't been used for years - too easy to get sliced from the village shop," said Mr Challen. There didn't appear to be a Mrs Challen.

"Been too busy with the sheep for housework today," said the old man, seeing my eyes stray to the wooden draining board over the stained butler's sink, which carried a disgusting array of dirty crockery, some equipment for mixing milk for orphaned lambs and a large hypodermic syringe. The plunger on the syringe was pressed home; for a minute I studied Mr Challen for the possible effects of heroin, before deciding that it had probably been emptied into some poor unsuspecting sheep - though on reflection there had definitely been something odd about the dog's eyes.

There was a strange smell in the room, redolent of sour milk, damp clothes and mice. Any minute I expected my usually fastidious husband to turn and leave; I was ready to go, but he seemed fascinated by the place and impervious to the smell.

The collie slid round the half open door, crouched close to the ground and stared at Gerald.

"Er - your dog," he indicated nervously.

"Get out you!" said the old man, kicking the door shut as the dog fled.

He took us into the sitting room where we both carefully ignored the Indian restaurant flock wallpaper in red and gold, and the shocking pink paint on the tongue and grooved pine door.

"This place is just perfect for us, isn't it darling?" said Gerald.

I was looking out of the tiny sitting room window. "Lovely view," I said, "but it's awfully steep."

"How else would you get such a stunning view? The house overlooks nearly all of its own land." He joined me at the window. "We'll get a picture window put in here."

Two long-legged spiders scuttled away into the limp, orange floral curtains as he gestured.

"Wouldn't that be rather out of keeping with the rest of the house?" I asked, but Gerald was expanding his idea to include French windows and a patio with a barbecue.

I caught the hastily controlled flicker of amusement that crossed the old man's face.

"We really don't need this much land just to walk the dogs, Gerald," I said, "and what if we get a heavy snowfall, how will we get up that steep track to the road?"

"You weren't listening the other night, when I tried to discuss this with you, were you? I'm tired of breathing traffic fumes. It's time we thought about where we want to spend the rest of our lives. If I can retire while I'm still reasonably young and healthy I would like to keep a few animals, help to conserve some rare breeds of farm animals, and for that we need land."

I had been listening; but as this ambition of his had come to light after several large gins in the bar where we were drinking with his secretary Hazel, and her partner Alan, I hadn't taken it seriously.

The extreme dilapidation and smell of the place were beginning to depress me and I wanted to get back out into the fresh air, even if it was cold. The old man was saying that bad winters were no real problem here in the south, and offering to sell us his old snow plough to fix to the front of our tractor.

Gerald didn't tell him that we had no tractor, as he

took him up on this kind offer.

"There, darling, no question of our getting snowed in." He put a comforting arm round my shoulders and gave me a squeeze.

"We don't know anything about looking after farm animals." I could hear my voice rising.

"Rare breeds, darling, only one or two rare breeds."

I pictured the sweet pygmy goats we had seen on a trip to the Miniature Pony Stud on Dartmoor, and the adorable, wrinkly, Vietnamese pot-bellied piglets - whilst carefully closing my mind to the memory of their enormous ugly mother - and suddenly realised that Gerald was asking the old man how soon he could vacate the place.

"Would you be wanting any of the stock?" said Mr. Challen.

"No," I said quickly, as Gerald's eyes lit up.

"I could leave you the dog – he's good with sheep. A well trained sheep dog'll cost you."

"No thanks – we've got our own," said Gerald hurriedly.

I had a mental picture of the dachshunds, Huggy, Rudi and Flicka, driving a flock of fleeing sheep over a cliff to their doom, and suppressed a smile. Gerald saw it and frowned at me to be silent.

"I'll show you the bathroom," said Mr. Challen proudly, "added it on a couple of years before I lost the wife."

He opened the door to a flat roofed extension leading off the kitchen, exposing hideous geometrically patterned linoleum in orange and blue, surrounding an old stained white bath on legs. In the opposite corner sat an equally unappetising toilet, graced with a cracked blue plastic seat and high level cistern. The chain had long ago lost its pull handle, which had been replaced by a loop of baler twine, greasy with use.

Mrs Challen had obviously been gone some time. Probably died in self-defence, I thought.

"Lovely," I said, as Gerald, for the first time since I had known him, seemed to be lost for words.

A glance out of the kitchen window as we moved through, showed the collie slinking past as it patrolled the house, waiting for Gerald like Captain Hook's crocodile.

My desire to giggle vanished as Gerald began to elaborate his plans for transforming what could be a rather beautiful old farmhouse kitchen, into an award-winning designer version, full of Italian tiles and French kitchen cabinets.

"All it really needs is a new Aga, and a large dresser," I said.

"You're weird; most women would be thrilled at the prospect of a beautiful modern kitchen."

"I'm not 'most women'," I said vaguely, as common sense told me we wouldn't be living there anyway.

If Gerald did eventually get some animals, the whole idea of caring for them on land that steep, and with the farm buildings right down at the bottom of the hill, was totally impractical; even I could see that. His job as a bank manager would keep him in town all day, and my stock handling knowledge was limited to that which could be comfortably fitted into a small dog bed.

"I'll show you the buildings at the bottom," said the old man, pulling on his boots and picking up a thumbstick.

If anything, it was even colder outside than it had been when we'd arrived. I pulled up my coat collar, wishing I had worn a scarf, and looked round for the collie. It was not immediately visible but I caught almost subliminal glimpses of it moving through bushes and behind walls, keeping pace with us as we descended the slippery track.

Gerald was too busy telling Mr Challen about his plans for conserving rare breeds to notice the dog. Phrases like 'South Devon cattle' and 'Oxford Down sheep' were leaving his lips with impressive authority, but I assumed he was just ensuring that the old man didn't try to sell us any of his animals, and ignored the warning bells that were beginning to ring at the back of my mind.

In answer to my query about the cottage across the way, Mr Challen said it was just a holiday home; the owners lived abroad and only used it about three times a year.

The buildings surrounding the bottom yard were as tumbledown as the stable and barn in the small top yard opposite the house.

"I keeps the animals down y'ere in winter, it's more sheltered." The old man swept an arm round the yard, and in the three-sided cattle shed some moth-eaten cows raised their heads from the musty hay they were picking at, and stared uncomprehendingly at us.

I wandered across to the other side of the yard to peer into the darkness of a low stable, roofed with rusting corrugated iron; Mr Challen followed me.

"Got a couple of calves in there."

"Oh, aren't they too sweet," I gushed, deciding to play the role of suburban housewife in which I could see the old man had cast me. Gerald was doing enough 'knowledgeable' farm talk for both of us.

"Jill!" Gerald's voice sounded strange.

"Where is he?" I asked.

"Barn, I think."

It was gloomy in the barn and it took a moment to re-focus after the sunlight; sparrows twittered in the rafters above the bales of hay stacked at one end. There was a flash of white as the collie moved and then I saw Gerald in the far corner. He was standing on an old disc roller, while the collie weaved from side to side, keeping him penned there.

"That *is* a good dog," I told Mr Challen. "Have you ever entered sheep dog trials with him? That deserves ten out of ten for penning."

"Get it off, Jill - and stop making silly remarks." It seemed that all this farming was causing Gerald to lose his sense of humour. At least this might put him off keeping sheep, I thought.

I couldn't have been more wrong.

The old man flung his stick at the dog, which disappeared behind the hay bales.

Giving a nervous glance round to make quite sure it had gone, Gerald climbed off the roller looking somewhat shamefaced. I thought it best to keep silent.

"You'll be wanting the hay, I expect. We can come to some arrangement about that... and this silage," said Mr. Challen, walking across to a huge black plastic mound covered with car tyres, at the end of the yard. He moved an anchoring tyre and pulled back a corner of the plastic covering, releasing steam into the cold air.

So that was the source of the sickly-sweet, fusty smell which had lodged in the back of my throat since we had entered the bottom yard.

"Yes, of course," said Gerald. I wondered if he knew what one did with silage. Did you feed it to the animals, or spread it on the land?

9

"Right – let's go back to the house," he said.

We started back up the hill. Our septuagenarian host reached the top yard a couple of minutes before us. Honour demanded that we had to pretend to be admiring the view halfway up, as we struggled for breath. My legs felt leaden and my lungs hurt, but at least the panting had cleared the cloying scent of silage from my nose.

"That's it then," I said. "I couldn't handle that hill on a daily basis."

"Look at him; he must be thirty years older than us. It's obviously something you get used to," said Gerald, wiping sweat from his scarlet face with a large handkerchief and trying to breathe normally, while his body struggled with the effects of too many business lunches. "Where's that bloody dog?"

"I don't know," I said, catching a glimpse of its tail as it slid round behind our car.

"Would you care for a cup of tea?" asked Mr Challen, as we followed him back into the sitting room.

Not out of that kitchen, I thought, hurriedly declining for both of us.

"Well - we are very interested in the place," said Gerald, turning away from me as I made frantic 'let's talk about this' signals.

"How soon do you think you would be able to move out?" he continued.

To try to control the look of horror I could feel had frozen on my face, I stared at a picture hanging crookedly on the wall. Through a festoon of cobwebs, I could make out some belligerent-looking, shaggy cows with enormous horns, set against a background of purple heather and mountains.

"Highland cattle, darling; you could have a couple

if you like." I suddenly began to wonder whether I knew Gerald at all; or, what was more to the point, whether he knew me.

The old man thought he would probably need about six weeks to organise a farm sale of the stock and implements which we didn't want.

"That sounds fine," said Gerald. I was shaking my head at him but he was ignoring me. I stopped signalling and turned to glare out of the window at the view. The collie caught my expression and slunk away round the corner of the house. Perhaps I do have a way with dogs, I thought, wondering how I could adapt it to deal effectively with Gerald, who was now telling Mr Challen that we would be going straight back to the estate agent to arrange the purchase of Warren Hanger.

As we left the house I realised I could hear the sound of water falling. It was coming from behind a small wooden door, which was set into the stone wall that ran between the side of the house, and the fields rising to the top of the hill.

Lifting the heavy iron latch, I pulled open the door to reveal a brick-built well, with water gushing into it from a stone spout just below the top. For a moment my feelings about the place wavered. There is something very soothing about the sound of running water.

The old man assured us that it was drinking water, and said that three generations of Challens had been reared on it, before the mains water had reached the farm.

Then he spoiled the idyllic moment by saying: "Course, you could always tell when the 'orse 'ad pissed in the top field."

The yard appeared empty as we took our leave. I got into the car while Gerald walked round to his side.

He opened the door, screamed, and jumped in with the collie hanging onto his right leg. He banged the door against the dog which yelped and fled, as Mr Challen appeared round the car with his stick.

"Dog get you?" he asked.

"Yes," said Gerald, through clenched teeth, trying to roll up his trouser leg to inspect the damage.

"He does that...thinks this is his yard. Right, you'll be in touch then?"

"Yes." Gerald was staring at two drops of blood oozing from puncture holes in his leg.

He turned the key, put the car into gear and pulled out of the yard saying that we had to find a chemist quickly.

"Is it bad?" I asked.

"I'm bleeding."

I offered to drive while he stemmed the flow of blood, and he slid the car to a stop on the muddy verge at the top of the farm track, muttering that the first thing he was going to do was get the drive tarmaced. The wound wasn't as bad as he'd made it sound, but it was stupid of me to point this out.

"It's very painful," he groaned, "and I've probably got rabies - that dog definitely wasn't sane. Did you see its eyes?"

"You'll be all right – we'll get some witch hazel to put on it, if we can find a chemist out here in the wilds. Now listen, Gerald, this is ridiculous - we can't live there."

His mind was taken from his wound while he explained how Warren Hanger Farm was the ideal place for us to start conserving rare breeds. The buildings were perfect, thirteen acres was enough for a few animals and, best of all, it was only a short distance from the mainline station to London. As an afterthought, he added that there must be heaps of dog shows out here in the country. I had just begun to show the dachshunds who had won some minor prizes. But I ignored this obvious 'carrot'.

"Who's going to look after these 'few animals' while you're in London?" I asked.

Another drop of blood trickled down his leg.

"Could we get moving now and find that chemist before my leg goes black and drops off?"

"That's gangrene - I thought you had rabies."

"Come on, quick; it's beginning to throb."

He clutched his leg above the wound - to stop the poison spreading, I assumed.

I put the car into gear, nearly stalling as we moved up the hill, and pointed out again that the land was cripplingly steep, and we knew nothing at all about farm animals. Gerald ignored this and tried to deflect me with a lyrical description of how beautiful the house would be when we'd finished modernising it.

Well, Gerald had been wrong about his diagnosis of rabies - and I had been wrong in thinking I could talk him out of buying the farm; which was how I came to be standing in the corner of a dark stable with my fingers up the nostrils of a very angry cow.

CHAPTER TWO

When we got back from Sussex that fateful afternoon, we took the dogs for a walk in the park.

"Surely life in the country would be better than this?" Gerald had shouted, competing with the noise of the London traffic as we made our way back towards the flat; he was limping slightly.

"Yes, but in a nice cottage like that one across the field," I yelled back over the revving engines and the coughing of the dogs who, being somewhat vertically challenged, had to live their outdoor lives at exhaust level.

"Derek has come back from Singapore," he said.

This sudden change of subject threw me for a moment. Gerald and Derek had been friends since they had worked together in Singapore. I had only met him briefly on one of his trips home, too short a time to form any real impression of him, but it was obvious that Gerald admired his rather carefree attitude to life.

"Yes, he's taken early retirement and bought a farm in Wales."

Suddenly it all became clear. Here was the reason for our trip to Sussex, and also the reason why Gerald didn't seem interested in pretty cottages. If Derek could buy a farm, so could Gerald.

"But if he's retired, it means he'll have time to farm. We wouldn't if you're still commuting," I pointed out.

"I'm only planning on a few animals to start with. Derek says it's a wonderful way of life. It'll be a challenge, it'll be fun."

14

I wasn't sure I was up to any more challenges. It had taken most of my nervous energy to escape from a disastrous fifteen-year marriage, and all I wanted now was peace and tranquillity.

My life for most of those fifteen years had consisted of constant tension and fear, as drink had gradually turned my ex-husband into a bully who, towards the end of our marriage, had also become physically violent. I was so embarrassed at making such a mess of my life, that I had tried to keep the worst parts of this relationship a secret from friends and my family, but it all began to come out when my mother suddenly had a heart attack.

This occurred the day after David had resorted to his fist, to make a point in a stupid argument we were having, which resulted in a spectacular black eye for me. There was no way I could hide the damage; normally I would have worn dark glasses and kept away from people for a few days, but I had to visit my mother in hospital and she patently didn't believe me when I said I had walked into a door.

Finally, when I began to fear for my life, I summoned up the courage to leave and, packing my son Max, the three dachshunds, and some duvets and pillows into my Mini, we ran away to stay with friends. David had always threatened to come after me when I had spoken about leaving before, but when I actually left he seemed at a loss to know how to cope with it. I should have left years earlier, but fear does strange things to battered wives.

I was at a very low ebb when I met Gerald two months later, at a party. He was there on his own and the friends I was staying with lost no time in telling me that he was divorced. Apparently his wife had got sick of living in Singapore and returned to England, where she had met someone else.

He seemed to be the opposite of everything I had left behind. Tall, slim and fair-haired, where David had been balding and running to a beer belly from the constant drinking.

I couldn't believe my luck when this confident, amusing man showed an interest in me, and I fell for him in a big way. When my divorce came through and he asked me to marry him I was in seventh heaven - finally I would be able to live a normal life like everyone else, I thought...Wrong! Well, to be fair, it had been all right for the first five years in London.

The cow moved and grazed my elbow against the wall; slimy mucous trickled slowly down the back of my hand and cooled rapidly in the chilly wind which was blowing into the stable. I began to shiver - this was not how I had planned to spend my days in the country.

One of Gerald's arguments which had helped to persuade me to move, had been that 'down in Sussex you'll have the peace to write that novel you're always talking about'. 'Always talking about' was a wild exaggeration. I seem to remember having become quite excited about the idea for a few days, after having had a piece published in a doggy newspaper; but when he'd mentioned it again, he had rekindled that small flame, and I had begun to find the idea very appealing: but, instead of chasing fame as a second Daphne du Maurier, I seemed to have become a farmer, something even my wildest dreams could never have predicted.

Five years of marriage to Gerald should really have taught me that he had a fairly low boredom threshold, and hobbies taken up with boundless enthusiasm seldom lasted long, but until now they had not involved live creatures which needed constant care and attention. The previous hobby, while we were still in London, had been wood-turning. After an initial purchase of some very expensive machinery, which he set up in the garage, he had produced two beautiful polished walnut bowls, and five pepper mills, all too tall, top-heavy, and disquietingly phallic. Gerald didn't seem to have noticed this aspect, but my sister Erica did when she and her husband Donald came to dinner, shortly before we first went to see Warren Hanger Farm.

Gerald had agreed to their visit with unusual eagerness, which I now realised was because Donald is a farmer. I hadn't known then about Derek's new venture in Wales.

So keen was Gerald to talk 'farming', that he had even allowed Erica to make fun of his pepper mills and given her one to take home, much to her embarrassment.

If I had known then that Gerald was seriously beginning to consider a move into farming, I would have pleaded with Donald to try and put him off.

Now it was too late, it had all happened; and my pathetic urge to please the man who had rescued me had landed me in this cold wilderness, and I missed Max. He was the only good thing to have come out of my first marriage, and somehow he had managed to grow up remarkably unscathed by the battles which had raged around him as a child. Now, just turned nineteen, he had decided not to move with us, and had started his first job as an apprentice electrician. I was finding it hard to come to terms with the fact that he really was capable of looking after himself. He had taken this opportunity to untie the apron strings, with the total confidence of youth, and moved into a flat with a friend. I missed his zany sense of humour, and strong sense of the ridiculous. Gerald can sometimes be a little pompous.

Max might have been persuaded to move with us, if it had been to my dream country cottage; but when he'd discovered that the nearest night club was thirty miles away, and Gerald began to delegate weekend duties, such as mucking out the animals, it had been enough to convince him it was time to leave home.

The wind whistled round the back of my neck. Max would have had hysterics if he could have seen me now - being a farmer.

Gerald, sitting in the comfort of his centrally-heated office, thought he too was a farmer. Even his secretary, Hazel, a very nice girl from North Finchley, who could wear a silk shirt better than anyone I knew, and had beautifully manicured finger nails, was being schooled by Gerald in the intricacies of beef management.

The cow bellowed, spraying me with hot, spittle-laden breath.

"Hang on to her," the chap at the other end said.

"I am hanging on," I muttered through clenched teeth, wondering what horrific disease one could contract from cow spit.

We had only just moved into Warren Hanger Farm when my current problems began. They arrived one

Sunday afternoon in a large lorry which belched blue diesel fumes across the small patch of front garden, as it slowly came to a halt in the farm yard.

"It's the cows, darling. Come on." Gerald's excitement was almost catching. We left the ancient refrigerator, which we had just extracted from the nettles in the garden and were trying to lift onto a wheelbarrow, and went to meet the driver.

I was detailed to shut the yard gate while the driver and Gerald opened the rear of the lorry. The driver then went inside and made encouraging noises, not unlike those made by the beasts themselves. There was a rustle of straw and a deep grunt, and the lorry swayed slightly; then down the ramp lumbered the first of Gerald's excursion into rare breed farming in the form of two enormous, identical, red cows. Even he looked a bit taken aback.

"My God, they're huge!" I gasped.

"They looked smaller in the pictures," he said.

Several times during the previous weeks, I had tried to point out to him that we knew nothing about cows, but he had confidently insisted that you could learn anything from books. My dreams of sweet little goats and piglets took a nasty lurch into reality as I gazed at these monsters.

The cows swung heavy heads round the yard sizing up their new home, one of them mooed in a half-hearted sort of way while the other raised her tail and deposited a stream of noxious brown cowpat on the new tarmac.

The dogs, safely confined behind a chain link fence in the back garden, barked furiously at the strange smell and sound of cow.

Reaching inside the cab, the driver picked up an envelope and handed it to Gerald, who opened it and drew out the registration documents for the two beasts. These certificates, which he proudly displayed, stated that the cows were South Devons, named Primrose 71 and Primrose 73. Spring was never going to be the same again for me.

I didn't want to think of a farm somewhere with at least 73 Primroses on it, and tried to pretend I wasn't afraid of cows - at least while the lorry driver was there.

He and Gerald, waving their arms and shouting: "Goo on!" drove the Primroses down the track and into a field halfway down the farm, where they wandered about pulling at the grass, with seeming unconcern at their change of circumstances.

I remembered that Nietzsche once said that he would like to ask cows the secret of their happiness, but it would be pointless as they would have forgotten the question before they could give an answer. It was probably best that they didn't know they had been delivered into the dubious care of two agricultural ignoramuses.

That evening Gerald subjected me to a crash course in cattle breeding, showing me glossy brochures containing stunning pictures of incredibly macho bulls, and said that the Primroses would be mated to a red Aberdeen Angus to ensure that their first calves would be both small and colour coordinated with their mothers.

"Of course, we won't keep these half-breeds," he said. He didn't actually say where the calves would go, and I didn't ask.

The following morning, after he had set off for London, I opened the sitting room window which overlooked the back garden, and drank in the view across our fields to the wood on the boundary. From the middle of this wood rose a column of smoke which hung on the still frosty air. Someone was having a bonfire, or maybe there was a cottage hidden in the trees. I pictured a cosy log fire, as I leaned on the window ledge taking deep breaths of clean air and enjoying the peace of the countryside, broken only by the sound of a distant tractor and the bellowing of a neighbour's cow. Probably had her calf taken away to market, I mused, wondering how Gerald would stand up to the crueller aspects of farming.

I suddenly realised the frantic bellows sounded too close for a cow on the neighbouring farm. They were coming from the direction of the Primroses' field. Convinced that one of them must have escaped, deserted her sister, and was probably heading back to South Devon - did cows have a homing instinct?- I banged the window shut, grabbed my jacket off a nail in the scullery, and rushed out of the house, accompanied by the three dogs who thought we were chasing something. Though unsure what, they were more than willing to give tongue until our quarry should show itself.

We ran down the ankle-twisting, rutted track to the field beside the wood. The cows were both still there. One was grazing peacefully, the other roaring over the hedge into the middle distance.

The dogs skidded to a halt. I had introduced them to the cows the evening before, without the protection of chain link fencing, and they had decided that cows were not the natural prey of dachshunds - and could possibly be dangerous.

Crossing the field I asked the roaring cow why she was making so much noise; bravely standing my ground as she marched up and bellowed in my face. The dogs disappeared into the wood and the excitements of a rabbit warren.

The other Primrose ambled over, sniffed her noisy friend and then mounted her. Were these lesbian cows? Echoes of the previous night's lecture returned. Could she be 'bulling'? Did they yell to every bull within a three-mile radius: "I'm ready, come and get me"? Why hadn't I listened properly?

Unable to remember what Gerald had said about this phenomenon, I returned to the house and pulled 'Better Beef Rearing' off the bookshelf - to find that cows are only in season for a few hours and if not mated the chance is missed for weeks. He'd been so keen to start on this beef rearing business...I needed advice. I telephoned his office and Hazel said sorry, he was in a meeting and had said he wasn't to be disturbed for a couple of hours.

"Is it a life or death situation?" she asked. I told her no, and said I would ring back later. I was on my own. Right...Gerald wanted to breed cattle...I had better see what I could do about it...time was running out for Primrose, who still sounded desperate.

Artificial Insemination is not listed under 'A' in the telephone directory. Scrabbling through paperwork on the desk I found a newly-opened file marked 'South Devons'. Inside this was a Milk Marketing Brochure with a phone number pencilled in the corner. Maybe they could help.

The voice at the other end of the line said: "Morning, A.I."

I tried to sound as if I knew what I was talking about.

"Er...we have a cow that's 'bulling' - Warren Hanger Farm."

"If you want a visit, you have to phone before eight o'clock."

It was nine thirty. By tomorrow Primrose could have gone off the whole idea of motherhood and I was in danger of failing my first test of animal husbandry, literally.

I began to stutter as I tried to think what to do. Sensing my panic, the man offered to contact the A.I. man on his car phone, interrupting my grateful thanks by asking which bull I wanted.

On safer ground here, I ordered a red Aberdeen Angus; then was thrown back into confusion as he told me they only had black ones. Explaining to him that these were South Devon cows so it had to be a red Aberdeen Angus, I asked where I could find one. I'll swear he was laughing as he said he thought there were a few in Canada.

Through the open window I could still hear Primrose roaring for a husband. There was a note of extreme urgency in her demands, so I settled for black. Partly for Primrose's sake, and partly because Gerald was not beyond coming up with expensive schemes for flying red Aberdeen Angus semen over from Canada.

As I replaced the receiver I realised the cow would have to be brought in for this operation, and the only secure place at this end of the farm was an old stable beside the barn in what we were beginning to call the top yard.

Leaning against the wall of this stable were two heavy old iron gates, which I dragged round to the door, and used to build a funnel to direct Primrose into this love nest. I finished tying them in place with orange baler twine and straightened up, rubbing a pulled back muscle. A robin, which had been watching me from its perch in the nearby oak tree, began to sing its thin little winter song, but apart from this, the farm was ominously quiet.

Shutting the yard gate to prevent Primrose going up the drive to the road when I brought her up, I set off back to the field, thinking I should have a stick; you never see people driving cows without a stick. Perhaps Gerald would get me one for my birthday.

Across the field the cows were grazing peacefully, side by identical side and I had no idea which one was which. I should have marked the noisy one in some way. Then one mounted the other. Right! I prepared to drive the one who was underneath, which seemed logical, at which point they reversed their positions. Now what?

I willed one of them to bellow. The clumsy, half-hearted mounting exercise finished, they dropped their heads to resume wrenching up grass with long rough tongues.

Looking round to make sure no one was listening, I attempted to imitate the bellow of a very randy bull.

Both looked up, then one came towards me, eyes shining and a green tussock of grass hanging out of the side of her mouth. Backing away, I bellowed, invitingly, again and she followed me out through the gate...then trotted past me and away up the track, forcing me to take a heart-thumping short cut over a field to get ahead of her and turn her into my funnel.

Primrose looked at the dark stable interior, then tried to jump out over the iron gate. I ran forward yelling, pushed her into the stable, slammed the door and leant against it panting.

"Well done!" said the A.I. man.

"God! How long have you been there?" I prayed

that he hadn't witnessed my bull imitation. He was young and handsome, with warm brown eyes, and a nice smile. Maybe farming wasn't so bad after all. I wished I'd had time to put on some make-up and that my face wasn't scarlet and sweaty from racing across the field.

Primrose glared at him, swishing her tail.

"Have you any means of securing her?" he asked.

I found an old halter hanging in the barn, and as she circled the stable at dizzying speed, we managed to get it on to her and tie her to a ring in the corner.

He left, saying he was going to get the straw. There seemed to be plenty of straw but he knew best. Finding that Primrose would stand still as long as I scratched her back, I watched my nails filling up with a greasy filth while I waited. Did Daphne du Maurier ever have nails like a collier?

He reappeared, carrying a thin metal rod in his mouth as he pulled on a long plastic glove. Ah! The metal rod was a 'straw'. I was on a steep learning curve now and must try not to display too much of my ignorance to this very competent young man.

Going behind Primrose he twisted up her tail, causing her to jump forward and shake her head at the restricting halter.

"Can you nose her?" he asked, through teeth clenched on the metal rod.

Nose her? What on earth did he mean? Catching my blank look he explained what he wanted. I was to put my fingers up her nostrils and hang on to the bit in the middle. He didn't realise he was asking this of a woman whose previous experience of stock handling had progressed no further than the de-fleaing of a small dog.

However, gritting my teeth, I pushed two fingers

and a thumb into Primrose's slippery nostrils and as I clenched my rather long nails on the central cartilage, she froze in horror.

"Good," he said. I felt an odd sense of achievement. There I was, in total control of this huge animal, with just a finger and thumb. I wasn't sure what he was doing at the other end, and chose not to watch.

Afterwards he asked me for her number, which, he explained, was tattooed inside her ear. As I struggled to find it, and Primrose struggled to stop me from so doing, he joined me, but it was impossible to read, being obscured by a layer of dirt.

"Have you got an old toothbrush?" he asked.

I ran indoors, into the bathroom and grabbed a toothbrush.

The A.I. man scrubbed the ear clean and pointed at the tattoo with the toothbrush, which now had orange bristles. He noted the number, refused a cup of tea and left, handing me a totally disgusting, muck-caked plastic glove for disposal as we walked towards his car.

I vowed to be better prepared for him next time. Next time - what was I thinking of? My knees were beginning to shake with delayed shock. Primrose was still tied to the ring in the corner of the stable and becoming increasingly peevish about the fact. During his lecture of the night before Gerald had said that the cows were 'halter broken', so I decided to lead her back to the field. But first I fetched some scissors and shortened the tassel at the end of her tail. At least for a while I would be able to tell them apart.

Once through the stable door she broke into a gallop and, as the rope burned the skin off my fingers, I understood, too late, that 'halter broken' meant only that she had worn a halter before; not been trained to walk nicely on a lead.

I was towed behind her until she had pulled all the rope through my hands; then, as she had the edge on me for speed, I had to let go. Thanking God that the A.I. man had not witnessed this example of my incompetence, I ran after her to where she eventually stopped at the gate to her field.

To prevent her from running away again before I'd managed to remove the halter, I tied the end of the long rope to the top rail of the gate, then opened it and eased her inside.

Before I could undo the halter buckle she took off again towards her friend, snapping the rail she was tied to as if it had been matchwood.

Trailing the rope, she managed to stay out of my reach for ten minutes, while I followed her round the field. Finally the loose rope caught between the claws of her hind foot and brought her crashing down onto her knees as she tried to avoid me. This allowed just enough time to undo the halter which fell off as she rose.

An excited burst of yapping from the wood filled me with guilt. In all the recent drama I had completely forgotten the dogs who were now in full cry after something.

A stressed-looking rabbit shot out of the wood and away across the field. Rudi and Huggy came out further along, having over-run the scent; they cast about for a minute, found it, and then followed it the wrong way, back into the wood.

It took a while, and some nasty bramble scratches, to persuade them and Flicka to come home with me. It hadn't taken them long to decide that their role in their new country life was to hunt.

Back indoors, I celebrated my first effort at farming

with a small brandy in my morning coffee.

I didn't ring Gerald; it would be easier to tell him what I'd done when he came home. But when he did arrive, he was so full of the excitement of his morning meeting, and the fact that he had persuaded a large firm to change their account to his bank, that I could hardly get a word in edgeways. It all seemed very high-powered and important compared with my day.

"Ugh, I can still taste that awful Italian stuff we had for lunch," he said, going into the bathroom. "Where's my toothbrush?" he called.

"It's on the ledge just inside the stable door," I told him.

"Do I want to know why?" he asked.

"It's a long story... there's a new one in the cabinet."

"Tell me about it in a minute," he said, coming back into the kitchen and picking up the torch. "I'm just going to see if the cows have settled in all right."

I got on with preparing supper, nursing my day's achievement to myself for a little longer.

"Something has broken the gate. I'll have to fix that at the weekend," he said as he came in. "The cows look all right though; one of them seems quite chirpy."

"That's 'cause she's pregnant," I said.

He'd got halfway through explaining to me that these were maiden heifers, so pregnancy was out of the question, before I managed to tell him about my day. Then he was upset because his firstborn calf was liable to be black.

"So's your eye if you don't stop moaning." I said, only half jokingly...I had expected praise for my initiative. "You have no idea how stressful today has been for me, Gerald. You can jolly well do the next one yourself."

"I'm sorry, darling," He relaxed. "Well done...it would have been nice to have a red calf, but it can't be helped. Can I get you a gin and tonic - or will you stick with the brandy?"

I knew I should have put the bottle away.

CHAPTER THREE

Two days later Gerald arrived home with a present for me.

"It's a 'thank you' for dealing with Primrose and the A.I. man," he said, placing a large box carefully on the kitchen table. "There's more," he said as he went back to the car.

I listened to the box already sitting on the kitchen table; nothing squeaked or scratched and I began to safely assume it didn't contain a rare breed. He shouldered open the kitchen door and placed a second box beside the first.

"Go on then - open them."

I pulled the sellotape off the largest box and discovered a word processor.

"There you go...now you can start the novel." He beamed at me.

Gerald was good at presents and he'd managed to give me exactly what I had wanted for some time. My old typewriter had been on its last legs for ages.

"Oh thank you, darling, you are clever. How did you know I'd been thinking about one of these?"

The other box held the keyboard and printer.

"It's second hand, but Hazel came with me to try it out and she says it's fine."

I got up very early the next day. This was going to be the start of my new life and a new career as a writer, now I had a purpose. I couldn't wait to start teaching myself how to use my new toy.

Gerald set off for work and had only been gone a

few minutes when the phone rang. It was him on his car phone.

"Don't forget the wor…" His voice faded into the buzzing which indicated that he'd driven into a blind spot, then the phone went dead. Oh well, if it was important he would ring back.

It was pouring with rain and, after a quick look out through the back door, the dogs refused to join me as I rushed out to feed the cows. I did minimal housework, prepared supper ready to the pop in the oven later, made a flask of coffee and took it to the desk in the tiny sitting room; then, opening the instruction book, I learned how to assemble the word processor.

I had just plugged the printer and keyboard into the computer, when there was a knock on the door; the dogs, using the pent-up energy they had not put into an early morning rabbit hunt, went overboard with a bout of aggressive barking.

A glance through the window showed a yellow van in the yard, with 'Burton's Electrics' written on it. In my excitement about getting started with the computer, I had forgotten the workmen were due to start that day. That was probably what Gerald had been trying to remind me on the phone.

"Charlie Burton…electrician," he said, looking nervously past me at the dogs. A sharp word from me had them wandering grumpily back to their beds.

The first thing Charlie did was turn off the power, instantly thwarting my plans for the day.

He was joined half an hour later by Roger the painter, Steve the carpenter / bricklayer, and Wayne the plumber, who turned off the water. Wayne's shaven head, laced-up boots and Arsenal shirt were a bit intimidating at first. I nearly didn't let him in, but Steve assured me that he was not in the least dangerous and was very kind to his mother. Gerald's big plans for renovating the house were under way.

I repacked the word processor in its boxes, and the days degenerated into chaos, masked by a haze of brick dust caused by Steve and his sledgehammer, as he demolished the dividing wall between the dining and sitting rooms, to create one decent sized room facing west.

He also knocked out the sitting room window, which we had decided to have enlarged. This gave a grand view - through grubby builders' polythene - away over the woods and the common to the whale-back humps of the South Downs.

One great disadvantage of builders' polythene is its total lack of insulating properties and, having created this hole in the wall, Steve found that there would be two weeks delay over the arrival of the window frame, as it was not a standard size. The cold permeated the whole house and too late we realised we should have left this stage of the rebuilding until the summer. Three mobile gas heaters helped a bit, but filled the house with fumes.

The dogs enjoyed having lots of people around to make a fuss of them. Our handsome black and tan Huggy became a silver dapple as a result of following Roger and his white paint roller all day. In fact, Hug looked rather like the negative of a sawn-off dalmation. He had discovered that Roger's lunch usually contained ham sandwiches, and occasionally a sausage; put in, I suspect, so that Roger could crack jokes about sausage dogs. I rapidly tired of these but Huggy proved an avid audience for this type of humour.

The smell of new paint and hot solder seemed to

permeate everything.

I didn't see a great deal of Charlie except for the hourly tea breaks, as he seemed to have taken up residence in the roof, accompanied by miles of electrical cable. Rudi eventually got tired of barking at the ceiling every time Charlie hammered in a clip.

While we waited for the new window frame, I had long conversations with Steve, who meantime had made a start on building the new kitchen cupboards. We spoke at length of 'two be twos', 'three be twos' and sometimes 'four be fours'. I hadn't realised that pieces of wood could be so exciting. Cooking was impossible, and Gerald and I took to eating our evening meal at the Royal Oak pub up in the village.

Wayne only talked about football and played radio one a lot on a cement dust-covered portable, until persuaded to bring his 'Walkman' instead.

Telephone chats with family and friends became uncomfortable, as they were either drowned out by the sounds of sawing and hammering, or intimate family details were aired at such a decibel level as to engage the attention of the nearest workman, who would obligingly signal his mates to 'down tools', just as I was shouting the latest hospital diagnosis of Aunt Edie's bladder problem to Erica. At which point it would emerge that they all had some family member with a similar, or totally unrelated, problem. Except Wayne. He only knew about torn cartilages and groin strains.

For relief I took to going up to the village shop, where the owner, Margaret, always had time for a gossip. She had run the shop for nearly twenty years, the last five on her own since her husband had died, but she was always cheerful. She knew everyone in the area, and all of their history back for several generations, and wasted no time in finding out about Gerald and me during my almost daily visits. Necessary trips, as I seemed to be constantly running out of tea bags and chocolate digestive biscuits.

It was during this upheaval that we met our neighbours, from their holiday-home cottage across the field, for the first time.

After a day spent clearing up after the builders, and disinfecting the stone floor in the scullery, for the third time since we had moved in, to try to remove the smell of whatever it was that Mr Challen's wellies had brought in over the years; and two trips down and up the hill carrying heavy bales of hay out to the cows, who had eaten most of the grass, I was decidedly weary by the time Gerald arrived home.

"We'll eat out," he said.

He quickly inspected the day's work on the house, while I dragged a comb through my hair with the last of my energy, and flopped into the warm comfort of the car seat with relief. It was short-lived. Jim, landlord of the Royal Oak, introduced us to the Barrington-Smythes.

Lavinia Barrington-Smythe took an immediate shine to Gerald, and her long blonde hair and impossible bust soon had him dribbling into his beer. The beautifully manicured scarlet claws had me sidling into the pub loo to try some temporary repair work with a nail file.

As I came back I heard Gerald telling her that I was a writer, and could cheerfully have strangled him. I was no nearer to being a writer than I had ever been and here was the luscious Lavinia asking me what I had had published recently. I waffled and she quickly returned to Gerald.

Piers Barrington-Smythe was short, self-important and seemed determined to explain the intricacies of investing in the 'futures' market to me. It was a relief when Jim told us our meal was ready.

By half past nine I was trying to smother my yawns and only just managed to stop Gerald inviting the Barrington-Smythes to join us for coffee, and persuade him to take me home.

"Nice couple," he said, as we drove out of the car park.

"Delightful," I agreed. He missed the sarcasm.

"Shame they're going back to Hong Kong tomorrow; it would have been fun to have them round."

"Mmm," I said. I'd rather invite the sheep in for supper, I thought.

Now I have to admit that the arrival of the first two sheep at Warren Hanger Farm was my fault.

CHAPTER FOUR

Just after we had arrived at the farm, we had fenced off a half-acre strip of the field between our back garden and the Barrington-Smythes' cottage, as a run for the dogs. But, dachshunds being somewhat low to ground, they were having difficulty with the neglected vegetation in this patch, which Mr Challen obviously hadn't used for some years.

The dogs didn't mind thick brambles when there were rabbits to be caught, but they weren't too keen on trying to negotiate thistles and stinging nettles woven together with dead couch grass.

Once let out into their paddock, they would disappear into the undergrowth, and the only evidence of their presence was the odd glimpse of flying ears, as they sprang into the air trying to see where everyone else had gone.

The builders began to play a 'spot the dog' competition during their tea breaks, and money would change hands betting on which head would appear first.

I had struggled to clear the paddock using a lawnmower then, worried by the strange noise the mower was beginning to make, had tried hacking at the vegetation using a rusty curved hook I had found hanging from a beam in the barn, where Mr Challen, or probably his grandfather, had placed it, by embedding the point in the wood. He later told me this was a 'fag hook'. It was indeed, and it very soon crippled my wrist.

"You want to get a goat or something to clear that lot," Steve said, reaching for the last chocolate biscuit. I made a mental note to pop up to the shop later.

This sounded like a good idea, but as Steve didn't know where I could find a goat, I telephoned Erica for advice...one of the advantages of Warren Hanger was that it was only seven miles from Erica and Donald's farm. This gave the comforting feeling that there was back-up knowledge there in case of emergencies.

"What about a couple of sheep?" she said.

"That could be the answer, but I don't need two, it's only half an acre - one would be enough."

"You can't have one by itself, it would be lonely...what about the twins I bottle reared last year? They've been ready to go to the butcher for ages now but I can't bear the thought. I've have been hiding them every time Donald selects a batch to go to market, and I'm afraid he's going to notice soon."

These two were orphans. Donald had taken their pregnant, but dying, mother to the hunt kennels to be put out of her misery, but, seeing movement inside her after she had been shot, had done an impromptu caesarean, with a butcher's knife, and delivered two premature lambs. These he had wrapped in a sack, and taken back for Erica to hand rear.

The first time I had seen them was when we had visited them last summer and Erica had taken me out to a field full of sheep; she was carrying two bottles which had once contained a rather nice Rioja, now filled with warm milk and surmounted by large teats.

She had called over the fence: "Come in 64 and 65." Two lambs with these numbers sprayed in red on their sides, had detached themselves from the flock and come bucking and racing across the field for their feed.

I still had that picture in my mind of little woolly lambs sucking furiously on the teats, tails wagging madly, as I accepted Erica's offer, and agreed to take both of them.

"I don't want any money for them, just give them a good home," she said. But I insisted on paying something and, after a short argument, managed to get her to accept a pitifully low price for the wether (a castrated boy sheep) - I was still on my farming learning curve - but she wouldn't take any money for the ewe, saying she was more trouble than she was worth as she had managed to escape from every enclosure on their farm.

That wouldn't present us with a problem as the fence round the dog paddock was impenetrable chain link and too high to jump. I arranged to fetch them the following morning.

Replacing the phone, it occurred to me that maybe I should have asked Gerald before going ahead with the sheep plan, but having picked up the phone with goats in mind, circumstances had rather taken over. These two sheep were not rare, they didn't even have pedigrees, but having agreed to save their lives, I couldn't back out now…whatever he said.

I would have to stress the fact that they were costing far less than a 'ride-on' motor mower to clear the paddock grass, but I didn't find a suitable moment to tell him about them that evening. He arrived home with a frown and a pile of paperwork from the bank, and made straight for the gin bottle. Then, drink in hand, he checked what the builders had achieved that day, and exploded when he found that Charlie had installed a power point in the wrong place in the sitting room; then he turned on me, wanting to know why I hadn't noticed what Charlie was doing.

Probably because I was busy buying sheep and

chocolate biscuits, I thought, as I promised to sort it out with Charlie first thing in the morning.

I decided to bring the sheep in quietly the next day without telling Gerald, and hope that he would have mellowed slightly by the time he saw them, and would appreciate that they were a good idea.

When I arrived to collect them, Erica found that the trailer I was to borrow had a flat tyre, so I decided to bring them home in the back of my estate car.

"Are you sure?" she asked doubtfully.

"Absolutely." I was keen to get on with clearing the vegetation in the dog paddock.

We lined the floor of the car with old plastic sacks, and built a sheep guard, using some chicken wire and baler twine, to stop them from joining me in the front seats. Then we manhandled these two rather smelly sheep out of a stable, and lifted them into the back of my car. They were heavy, and a lot larger than I remembered, and had definitely lost their 'Aah' factor.

Waving goodbye to Erica, I set off, trying to ignore the grin she was attempting to hide.

The only sound from my new lawn mowers, for the first two miles along country lanes, was the non-stop rattle of dung pellets and trickle of urine onto the plastic sacks. The car rapidly filled with clouds of choking ammonia fumes and I tried to breath only through the gap in my window.

They became vocal when we got held up by traffic in a small market town, sticking their noses through the open three inches of the windows, and imploring the passers-by for help. Everyone was pointing at me and it seemed to take hours to get home, but finally I was rattling over our cattle grid and onto the farm drive, with a sigh of relief.

I drove carefully into the dog paddock over the uneven ground, and got out and shut the field gate, before opening the tailgate of the car. The ewe jumped straight at me, knocking me flat on my back in the mud with her shoulder, and galloped away.

"You all right?" Steve called from the dining room window.

I gave him the thumbs up sign as I picked myself up and turned back to the car, determined not to give in to the pain in my shoulder blade, where it had landed on a rock. The wether stood there watching me, waiting politely to be helped down, and I fell in love with him.

"You lovely boy...you're much nicer than your horrid little sister, you were cheap at the price," I told him.

This was how these two came to be named Cheap and Nasty.

When I got indoors I made the builders swear not to tell Gerald I had used the car as a livestock transporter, and gave them all a large slug of brandy in their morning coffee.

When Gerald came home that evening he was less than pleased about the new additions.

"What kind of sheep are they?" he asked, sneering at them through the dining room window.

"White woolly ones."

"Don't be facetious...why didn't you wait? You knew I wanted 'Oxford Downs.'"

"They are just mowing sheep, Gerald... they are half bred something or others, I can't remember what Erica said. I've no intention of breeding from them, they're just for keeping the dog paddock clear."

He wasn't impressed by my rather weak excuse that I had saved them from the butcher, but brightened up at the word 'butcher' - I didn't like his expression, there was a hint of mint sauce in it.

With hindsight, or rather hindsmell, bringing them home in my car had not been such a clever idea and, even though I washed and disinfected every surface, it still took about three weeks of driving with all the windows open to get rid of the smell. Fortunately Gerald didn't borrow my car in that time, nor did he ask how the sheep had arrived.

The dog-proof chain link fence round the paddock kept Nasty in, and the dogs kept their distance from the sheep - after an initial concerted sheep-worrying attack from the pack had resulted in Rudi and Flicka getting stepped on, as Nasty tried to attack them back. Their blood-chilling screams caused Huggy to decide that sheep were just as dangerous as cows, and the three of them stayed well clear of the larger farm animals after that.

The two sheep made a good job of clearing the overgrown vegetation, then began to run out of grass and had to be moved to a fresh field for a while. The other dilapidated fencing on the farm proved no obstacle to Nasty and, as she went back to her old hobby of escapology, we became used to finding her wandering around the place, though she never went very far from Cheap who, of course, being perfect, stayed where we had put him.

Cheap was already very tame from having been hand reared, and I taught him to wear a halter and to walk beside me on a loose lead. He became better trained than the dogs. Nasty, though semi-tame, seemed convinced that I was trying to inflict some mortal injury on her by putting the halter on and, when restrained, leapt about on the end of the rope like a hooked fish, before collapsing in a faint. She would follow her brother though, so moving them around the farm was easy, as she trotted free behind us.

One day, investigating a clattering noise from the feed store, I was confronted by a bucket with ears, which baa-ed hollowly at me. As I laughed, the bucket waved around trying to pinpoint the sound of my voice. In her greedy haste to salvage a few sheep nuts left in the bottom, Nasty had managed to hook the handle behind her ears, trapping her head in the bucket. I removed it and, instead of being grateful for her rescue, she glared at me and marched off in a huff. Sheep don't like being laughed at.

Although she could escape from virtually anywhere, she could never get back in and, when tired of wandering, she would find me, and demand that I open the gate for her so that she could rejoin her brother. I had thought this habit was rather endearing in one who, most of the time, was totally unco-operative and bloody minded, until one morning when I was up a ladder in the barn, pulling a bale of hay from the top of the stack.

I could hear the tapping of little cloven hooves coming closer on the concrete yard, then Nasty marched round the corner.

"Baa - THERE you are," she said.

"Go away!" I shouted as she headed for my ladder.

"Baa," she said, squeezing between the ladder and the stack.

I clung desperately to the string on one of the stacked bales, but the bale came away with me as the ladder swung out. I struck Nasty on the way down, and lay there winded, struggling for breath and mentally testing bits of myself for mortal injury.

She stared down at me as if I should apologise for

carelessly hitting her with my head, then having attracted my attention, she went back to the field gate and waited for me to let her in with Cheap.

The building workforce was really very sympathetic when I limped back into the kitchen. Steve suggested he should 'rub it better' and made me a cup of coffee; while Wayne offered to go out and kick Nasty into submission. I didn't have much trouble declining Steve's offer, but was sorely tempted by Wayne's.

When I showed Gerald my bruises that evening, he seized on the opportunity to suggest that I got rid of "that bloody ewe of yours". Apparently he had had to stop the car on his way up the drive that morning and persuade her to move from where she was dozing in the sun, before he could pass. It had nearly made him late for the train. Nasty had quickly discovered that the tarmac on our new drive absorbed the sun, and made a perfect warm under-blanket for a snooze.

Much as I would have liked to pass Nasty on to a good home, I was becoming very fond of Cheap who was kind and gentle, and never did anything wrong. I couldn't lose Cheap, and he would be bereft without his sister. We were stuck with her.

I would have to make sure the drive was clear for Gerald each morning, even if it meant walking ahead of the car with a red flag... or perhaps one of those electric cattle prods I had seen advertised in his farming magazine.

CHAPTER FIVE

To escape from the dust and clatter of the builders, I had taken to walking the dogs across the field just below their paddock, and climbing through the fence into the wood behind the Barrington-Smythes' cottage. About twenty feet inside the wood there was a fallen tree beside the stream, where I could sit and relax while the dogs hunted for mice and rabbits in the undergrowth. This was where I met Conor for the first time.

Lulled into a semi-hypnotic trance by the ripple of the water running between mossy rocks, and thinking of nothing in particular, I was suddenly shocked into adrenalin-pumping life by an angry voice behind me.

"Is this yours?"

As I slipped and struggled to my feet, trying to disentangle my jacket which had hooked on a protruding branch, a shocked-looking Huggy, suspended by the scruff of his neck, was thrust into my face.

All I could stutter was: "Don't hurt him, he's only little."

"Hurt him! I'll shoot him if I find him round my pheasants again."

The content of this remark was tempered slightly by a soft Irish accent. But the face was unsmiling, and he looked as if he meant it.

He pushed a frightened Huggy into my arms, where he quivered, and plastered the front of my waxed jacket with mud and pheasant droppings.

I should have apologised, but I found myself mesmerised by a pair of piercing blue eyes under the peak of a tweed cap. The hair which escaped from the cap was black and wavy above a lean, deeply tanned and very stern face. The hand which released its grip on Huggy was surprisingly long and elegant.

Where were the other two dogs? I couldn't hear them. I put Huggy down and bent to clip the lead onto his collar, whilst framing a suitably grovelling apology, but when I looked up the man had gone, as silently as he had arrived.

As I wondered where his pheasant pens were, so that I could avoid searching for Rudi and Flicka in that direction, they came sneaking out of the undergrowth, glancing nervously about to make sure he had gone.

I found I was shaking; too many years married to an aggressive man had taken its toll on my nerves. Once more I blessed my luck in having escaped from David.

The builders didn't seem to know who this man was, but they didn't live in the village. It was Margaret at the shop who told me his name, and that he lived alone in a cottage deep in the woods where he worked for the Forestry Commission. It must have been from this cottage that I had watched the smoke rising in the frosty air.

She said that Conor Ahern was a bit of a mystery. He'd arrived about a year ago and mostly kept himself to himself, though he did visit the Royal Oak occasionally, usually with another man, and the two would spend the evening deep in a quiet, private conversation.

"Irish he is," said Margaret. " There's some as say he's got something to do with the IRA. Doesn't seem to have a wife, he lives alone. There was a woman once, used to come over on the Chichester bus and visit him, but I haven't seen her for some time now." Margaret managed to make this last remark sound sinister.

Gerald didn't seem very impressed when I told him about my small adventure in the wood, and showed no signs of rushing off to remonstrate with Conor for frightening me. As to the threat to Huggy's life, he would probably have shaken the man by the hand for that; he's never really liked Huggy who reciprocates the feeling. Both of them think they own me, and they are jealous of each other.

Gerald brushed my story aside, and said I should keep the dogs on a lead, or in their run. He was much more worried by the fact that Hazel and Alan had gone to California for two weeks, and he was having to make do with a 'temp', who was apparently quite useless, and not at all interested in farming.

I went to bed that night feeling ever so slightly un-cherished, except of course by Huggy.

The second Primrose started bellowing at about four o'clock the next morning. As it was Saturday I naturally assumed that Gerald would deal with the problem and at seven o'clock he went down to the field to look at the cow.

"Yes, she's definitely bulling; they're climbing all over each other. You'd better ring the A.I. and organise things. I'd do it but I've got to go and look at a tractor."

"Tractor?" I said blankly.

"Of course; what's the good of a snow plough if you don't have a tractor to fix it to?"

I didn't want to have to cope with the A.I. man again - beyond asking him in for a cup of coffee when he had finished. Steve had nearly completed the

46

building of the kitchen, and I welcomed every opportunity of showing off the new pine cupboards, green-tiled worktops and shiny black and gold Aga, to visitors.

"They're your cows, Gerald...I thought you wanted to be a farmer."

"Well, you know what to do. And you're good at it."

"Flattery won't get my fingers up another cow's nose - you do it."

For too long, I thought, I have let Gerald talk me into doing things I didn't really want to. There was a limit to my gratitude for being rescued from my single impecunious state, and I was beginning to reach it. I decided I had to make a stand before things went too far, and I became a doormat again.

He didn't react to this very well. Gerald's main role in life is delegation - especially of the dirtier jobs, I was discovering - but I held my ground, and explained the procedure for getting the cow into the stable.

His mouth tightened as he listened, then he telephoned Mr Challen, who had moved to a bungalow in the village, and coaxed him out of retirement for the morning to assist him.

I had polished the kitchen, combed my hair and sprayed on a subtle amount of perfume - the A.I. man wasn't going to catch me out again - when there was the sound of several pairs of footsteps in the scullery, and I heard Gerald offering them coffee. Mr Challen came in first as if he still owned the place, followed by the A.I. *girl*!

She was about twenty years old, slim, with a small elfin face framed by short dark hair. She grinned at my ill-concealed surprise.

"I know; you were expecting Jeff," she said. Gerald was looking smug.

Mr Challen gazed around at the waxed pine cupboards and white walls; it had taken a lot of effort to get rid of the red and blue paint.

"Is that the undercoat?" he asked, and then described how he had just finished decorating his new kitchen. Orange walls and a lovely bright blue on the cupboards. The red and black vinyl floor just "set it off nice".

The elfin girl's name was Sam, and I warmed to her as I caught her suppressing a smile at the image of Mr Challen's kitchen. The three dogs took to Sam as well because she fed them pieces of chocolate biscuit under the kitchen table. Watching this, Mr Challen told me he had never let his dog in further than the scullery, "on grounds of hygiene".

"Mind if I smoke?" he said and, without waiting for an answer, pushed his coffee mug to one side and took from his pocket a rusty old tin, and a packet of cigarette papers. He laid these on the table in front of him and began an elaborate ritual of carefully aligning strands of tobacco from the tin, along the small piece of paper which he had smoothed onto the table. I'm not sure why he smoothed it out so carefully, because, having placed a minute amount of tobacco onto it, he rolled it up into a crumpled tube, which he then licked, wetly, and sealed. The resulting cigarette was about as thick as a thermometer. He struck a match and held it to the end of the 'roll-up', which was mostly paper, and it flared frighteningly until the tobacco caught.

"That's better," he said after a deep drag which burned away at least a third of the cigarette, and made the dogs sneeze.

I tried to remember where I had put the ashtrays. Gerald and I had both given up smoking some years before, and as so few people smoked nowadays I tended to forget to put them out. But at that point Sam got up to go. Apparently she had more unfortunate cows to impregnate.

Then Gerald and Mr Challen left to look at the tractor - which we would only need in case of deep snow. I forgot to ask Gerald, before he left, whether he had ever driven a tractor. It probably wouldn't have been a tactful question in front of Mr Challen, and I could sense that Gerald was still displeased with me over the stand I had taken about mating the second Primrose.

As long as everyone agreed with him life was sweet, but cracks had begun to appear in his relationships with those who didn't; beginning with Huggy and recently extending to "that bloody ewe of yours".

Of course Cheap and Nasty were at a strong disadvantage with Gerald, as they had no idea who their parents were. In an odd way, he seemed to find their lack of pedigree embarrassing: he didn't want them on the farm, and I was having to fight to keep them. He lost no opportunity of trying to persuade me to replace them with a pair of rare Oxford Down sheep, but, even if I'd wanted to do this, there was nowhere safe for Cheap and Nasty to go. If I took them back to Erica, Donald would send them to market, and I couldn't have that on my conscience.

An hour later a small ancient tractor, driven by Mr Challen, trundled down the drive, followed by Gerald's car. The tractor looked very like the one which had stood in the yard when we first visited the farm, and its tyres exactly fitted the ruts where Mr Challen now expertly parked it.

When I mentioned this coincidence to Gerald later, he assured me that the tractor had belonged to 'a bloke called Sid' who had used it to haul wood when he was felling timber in the chestnut copses. He'd had it for years, apparently.

Gerald made no attempt to drive the tractor that day, though he spent a lot of time looking at it and telling me that it was a Ferguson TVO which, when done up, would be worth a lot of money to any collector of vintage tractors. He thought he might have a go at this renovation task himself, when he had time. As Gerald wasn't very good at getting dirty, I thought we might have Fergie, as he called it, around for quite a while.

The tractor looked so natural parked against the wall of the barn that I had almost forgotten its existence when, several days after its arrival, I found a brochure from Brinsbury Agriculture College on the desk. There was a pencilled ring round a course called 'Tractor Driving for the Farmer's Wife'. I buried the brochure under a pile of papers in the desk drawer and hoped Gerald would forget about it. I had seen the 'play' in that tractor's steering wheel as Mr Challen had turned it into the yard, and there was absolutely no way Gerald was going to persuade me to get into the driving seat, an uncomfortable wrought iron affair, draped in an old sack.

CHAPTER SIX

Suddenly, after all the noise and disruption, the builders had finished and left. For a day or two the silence seemed strange, and I found myself still putting the kettle on every two hours. The dogs wandered around disconsolately, sniffing out occasional chocolate biscuit crumbs which the vacuum cleaner had missed. The house smelled of paint and new carpets, and though I had been full of ideas about what I would do when the workforce finally left, I was finding it difficult to start anything.

Then Erica came over bringing a bottle of wine and arms full of housewarming flowers. This was what the place had lacked.

Once we had arranged vases of daffodils and irises in the new living room with its white walls and pale green carpet, the shiny new house began to turn into a home; the blue and yellow of the flowers picked out the dominant colours in the furniture covers and curtains.

We opened the wine and spent a pleasant afternoon discussing curtains, husbands, dogs, sheep and enigmatic Irishmen in the woods.

"It all sounds very exciting. How do I get to see him?" Erica asked.

"You could try barking at his pheasants," I told her. By this time the bottle was empty and we were both at a comfortably silly stage of our impromptu housewarming. "Anyway," I went on, "that's probably the last exciting thing that will happen around here now. It's very quiet without the builders."

"Well, you can put that machine together and start writing your book. What's it going to be about?"

"I don't know." This was true. Various plots had suggested themselves while I listened to Gerald snoring at two o'clock in the morning. But mulled over in the cold light of day they had all been flawed and unworkable. "Perhaps there won't be a book and I'll end up using the computer to do the farm accounts."

"With two cows and two sheep that won't take long," Erica grinned.

"Why don't you stay and have some supper? We'll open another bottle and you can stay the night. Gerald's gone to Birmingham, he's not coming back until tomorrow."

"What's he doing in Birmingham? Not buying more cows, I hope."

"Good God, no! Two's plenty. He's got some meeting or other, I forgot to ask. Pass me the corkscrew."

After Erica had left in the morning, I settled down to make new curtains for our bedroom. The ones we had brought from London, and used until the decorating was finished, were too long, and I had never really liked them well enough to spend time altering them to fit the new windows. Not being a great seamstress, I had already spoilt several yards of material in attempting to cover the bathroom windows, but these promised to be more successful. This time at least I managed to get the pattern the same way up on both curtains.

The following afternoon they were finished, and I was standing on a chair at the window hanging them, carefully linking the hooks through rings on the smart mahogany pole. Putting the pole up had been the last job Steve had done, before collecting up some unused 'two be twos', and slowly setting off up the drive, carefully circumnavigating Nasty who was sunbathing on the warm tarmac.

It was a sunny afternoon, and from my elevated vantage point I could see across most of the farm to the stream on the boundary, then over the top of the wood to the common beyond. It was too nice to be indoors, and I promised myself a walk with the dogs later.

Cheap and Nasty were grazing quietly in a field near the house. The two Primroses, red coats gleaming in the sunshine, were lying in the bottom field by the wood, lazily chewing cud. Downstairs the dogs were having their afternoon sleep on the rug in front of the Aga. This was what we had come to the country for, a timeless peace and order.

Slipping another curtain hook into a ring, I was idly watching the police dog handler tracking across our bottom field towards the Primroses, when my relaxed brain suddenly engaged.

POLICE DOG HANDLER? Were they after Conor? Had Margaret blown his cover? I shot downstairs and out of the back door in time to see a white police van come speeding down the drive. Two more uniformed men with dogs leapt out and set off after the first, and a sergeant came over to me.

"Have you seen a man come through here about quarter of an hour ago?" he asked.

"No...what's happened?"

He explained that they were searching for an escaped prisoner, who had been disturbed whilst breaking into a house up on the common, and had run off in this direction. The first police dog had tracked him down to the farm, and was now following the scent along the course of the stream where it crossed our land. The police set up a radio base in the bottom yard, and soon a helicopter appeared and proceeded to circle the farm and common.

The postman arrived after a while with the information, gleaned in the shop, that the 'escaped mad rapist' had gone through the housing estate in the village. There he had stolen a small girl's bicycle, cycled to the station and taken the London train.

When I passed this story on to the police sergeant, he didn't seem very impressed. He was more worried about the fact that the first dog handler had been attacked by the Primroses in the bottom field, and had had to release his dog, which was now missing.

The helicopter suddenly left its circling, and set off in a straight line flying towards the downs.

"I see the helicopter's gone; have you found him?" I handed the sergeant the cup of tea I had taken out to him. He had been left to man the radio.

"No, we had to send it back...we can only afford to rent it for an hour."

I walked back to the house, taking a short-cut through the barn, musing on the impecuniosity of the Sussex Constabulary and wondering if the 'mad rapist' might have hidden himself on the farm somewhere. A movement from the top of a stack of straw bales in a dark corner caught my eye, and a dusty ray of sunlight, shining through a broken tile, glinted for a moment on the pair of eyes watching me.

"Help!" I whispered through a totally constricted throat. The bale moved and a pale face peered over it. I'm going to be murdered here, I thought, surrounded by policemen. I now know what is meant by 'frozen with fear'. The face moved, the evil eyes again glinting in the sun, the mouth opened.

"Baa!" it said.

"Nasty! You idiot sheep! What are you doing up there?"

"Wolves!" she baa-ed as my shaking hands dragged her off the bales, and pushed her out of the barn and back towards her field, while she gazed nervously around, searching for the tracker dogs. I'm not sure which of us was more afraid.

The afternoon drew into evening, and the police vehicles were still parked in the yard when Gerald came home. He spent a long time chatting to the sergeant, telling him all about the cows and his plans for the farm. The sergeant showed polite interest but I got the impression he was not over-fond of cows, especially as police dog Zoltan was still missing.

As dusk fell, two dogs and three handlers returned to the farm empty-handed, and Gerald asked them all in for coffee - or a drink. They looked at each other and settled for coffee.

They were in a somewhat bedraggled state after crossing and re-crossing the stream, and refused to use the chairs, sitting instead in a circle on the kitchen floor. They began extolling the virtues of the missing Zoltan. By this stage Zoltan was 'missing, believed dead'. Apparently it's very easy to kill a dog, and by the time they had finished explaining the method in detail, I was feeling slightly sick and decided a small brandy would not come amiss, whatever they were all having.

Seeing me reach for the bottle, Zoltan's young handler changed his mind and, fighting back tears, asked if he could have a brandy as well. This opened the floodgates and they all thought "just one wouldn't hurt". It had the effect of rendering them more maudlin than ever.

They recalled a particularly dangerous arrest Zoltan had made, in spite of having been stabbed by a drug pusher who was trying to escape his jaws. He had received a medal for this. He was a brave and true friend, they said, who wouldn't harm a soul... except in the line of duty. The sergeant patted Zoltan's handler comfortingly, as the lad was now sobbing openly.

None of them seemed to be giving a thought to the 'mad rapist', currently on the loose somewhere on a small girl's bicycle, if the postman was to be believed. But it didn't seem the right moment to bring this up.

They left eventually, promising to return the next morning to search the stream and overhanging vegetation for Zoltan's body.

At first light they were back, and set to work along the bank of the stream with fag hooks and slashers, felling the stinging nettles and brambles.

I took some hay to the Primroses, and tipped a bucket of sheep nuts into the trough in Cheap and Nasty's field; then made a flask of coffee and took it down to the bottom yard. The dog handlers were all back by their vehicles, smiling broadly.

"Have you found him?" I asked. None of them thought I meant the robber. They told me they'd just had a message over the radio saying that Zoltan was all right.

The vicar of Longham had been walking past his church that morning when he'd heard a strange noise. On opening the door, he found Zoltan. Apparently the robber had realised the dog was still following him, lured it into the church and shut the door, and there Zoltan had stayed for the night.

Longham was four miles away across the common, in the opposite direction from the station and the London trains, which rather spoilt the postman's theory.

CHAPTER SEVEN

The farm seemed very quiet for the next few days. Nasty stayed in her field, never far away from Cheap, and every few minutes she would look nervously down towards the stream.

Although having the house full of builders had been very intrusive, now that they had gone I missed their company and, like Nasty, found I was keeping a wary lookout as I went around the farm. I tried to settle into the daily round of getting Gerald's breakfast, then feeding the animals before walking the dogs. I had my breakfast around eleven thirty in the morning when I stopped for a break. I had always eaten with Gerald before, but now I found that trying to push a heavy wheelbarrow laden with hay for the cows was not to be recommended on a full stomach.

Leaning on the gate watching them one morning, after struggling with the load, I wondered why I bothered. I had cut the twine on the bale, spread biscuits of hay on the ground for them and stayed for a brief pre-natal chat, trying to establish some sort of rapport. But all they did was trample the hay into the mud and ignore my existence.

Fed up with the cows, I liberated the word processor from its box, and tried to make some sense of the book which was going to teach me how to use it. But after a couple of days of looking at it, and worrying about it, I packed it away in the box again. Spring was coming, there would be plenty of time for writing in the dark winter evenings, once we were really settled in.

Gerald seemed to be having similar problems with learning to drive the tractor. Occasionally he would start it up and run the engine for a while, to "stop it seizing up" he said. "No point in moving it at the moment" as there was nothing he needed to do with it until next winter.

One Friday Erica rang up. "I'm bored," she said. "How about a trip to Chichester tomorrow? We could shop, have lunch somewhere nice, then shop again."

This was just what I needed, and having put the idea to Gerald that evening, was surprised to find him in favour, even to the tune of giving me some money. This was unusual as he generally liked having me around at the weekends; I came in handy for supporting fence posts while he hammered them in, and acting as his farm hand if he wanted to move the cows to another field. This, quite apart from providing meals and snacks at regular intervals during the day.

"What have you got planned for today?" I asked him as we were getting dressed.

"Oh, nothing much, just a few odd jobs around the farm. There's a gate latch wants fixing." He was avoiding my eyes, a sure sign that there was a plan afoot that he didn't wish me to know about. I suspected he was going to use my absence for some tractor driving practice, and prayed that he would stay away from the steeper slopes.

Erica and I had a very pleasant time in Chichester, strolling around in the sunshine. The pedestrian precinct was bustling with shoppers, enlivened by groups of buskers, ranging from didgeridoo players, through jazz groups to solo violinists playing classical music. We had a light lunch and spent too much money on things we didn't need; altogether a most enjoyable day.

When I arrived home, refreshed by the change from my usual routine, I was relieved to see the tractor parked in its usual place in the yard. It was a warm sunny evening, and the tranquility of the farm was a balm after the noise and bustle of the city.

My relief that Gerald had not had an accident with the tractor, and that all seemed to be well, was short lived.

I took the dogs through the garden for a run in their paddock, and was shocked to find that it had been turned into an ovine battlefield - and it was immediately clear why Gerald had wanted me out of the way for the day. He had returned my presenting him with a 'fait accompli' when I got Cheap and Nasty, with a vengeance.

My gentle Cheap was standing in a corner looking woebegone, blood trickling down his forehead and, over by the fence next to the Barrington-Smythes' cottage, Nasty was desperately fighting for her honour. Six half grown lambs were huddled nervously together in the middle of the paddock; the seventh newcomer was a ram - judging by the attention he was paying to Nasty.

Gerald appeared, dressed in brand-new blue overalls and carrying a hammer. I jumped up and down and screamed rape - on Nasty's behalf - while he stayed cool calm and manly in the face of this wifely hysteria.

He assured me that the lorry which had brought the new sheep from Oxford had only just left, and he had put them into the dog paddock for a few minutes while he fixed the gate latch on the other field, prior to moving Foxbridge Henry, the ram, away from the ewe lambs. He went on to explain, soothingly, that Henry had not raped Nasty because he had been watching them all the time.

Trying to control the panic in my voice, I said that Erica had told me that with sheep, you only had to blink and you would miss it, and insisted he get Henry out, pointing out that he'd already given Cheap a head-butt worthy of a football hooligan.

Quickly shutting the dogs in the house again, I dashed back out to the paddock and chased Henry away from Nasty. She ran and hid behind Cheap, who began to look worried, as well as injured. Henry trotted back to the ewe lambs and checked them over to see if there was any work for him there yet. Fortunately, or unfortunately if you were Henry, they were still too young.

Gerald came back from his gate repairs to help me get Henry away from the ewes and out of the paddock, but the ram had no intention of leaving them. Gerald called, "Henry!" from an invitingly open gate. This proved an unproductive exercise because nobody had ever bothered to tell Henry what his name was. We were going to have to drive him out.

We circled the milling sheep and tried to cut Henry out of the flock, but this didn't work either - for a tubby ball of wool he was surprisingly fast.

Somebody whistled and shouted: "Come bye!" from the wood behind the cottage garden.

"What was that?" said Gerald.

"I don't know," I panted. "Did it have an Irish accent?"

It is all very well admitting to oneself that one is hopelessly incompetent at farming; but it is quite a different thing to be mocked by an outsider. My sense of humour deserted me, and I decided that Conor was a totally unlikeable character. I hoped the police or the IRA would catch up with him. I hadn't felt comfortable walking the dogs since he had shouted at me that day in the woods.

Chasing Henry was obviously a waste of time, and we stood for a minute trying to catch our breath, then I had an idea, and ran to fetch Cheap's halter.

As Henry seemed to be a bit of a thug, and had already seen Cheap as a rival, I wondered if we could tempt him out with the prospect of another 'punch-up'.

Leaving Gerald on gate duty, I led a nervous Cheap across Henry's line of vision. The ram's head came up, he hitched up his shoulders, arched his neck and began a macho walk towards us; as he broke into a trot and Gerald swung the gate open, Cheap and I ran.

Henry caught us as we went through the gate of his new field, slamming into Cheap's backside. Cheap turned, wrenched the rope out of my hands and ran back up the track. I slammed the gate shut in Henry's face.

"Gotcha mate!"

Sucking my bleeding, rope-burned fingers, I leaned on the gate trying to get my breath, whilst Gerald retrieved Cheap and led him back to the ewes.

Henry set off to explore his new home. Three sides of the field were fenced with old galvanised wire sheep fencing, and the fourth boundary was the stream. Gerald had been busy, as this was now guarded by a two-strand electric fence connected to a shiny new box, which on closer inspection revealed itself to be an 'Electric Shepherd'.

There are times when I hate having a literal mind. Passing that road sign that says 'Heavy Plant Crossing' is another of them.

As Gerald joined me at the gate to admire his ram, I demanded to know why he hadn't told me he had arranged to double our stock numbers.

"I wanted to surprise you," he said.

"O.K. I'm surprised. Who's going to look after them?"

"It's not as though there are hundreds of them; we'll both look after them. Seven's not a very large flock. I thought you liked sheep."

"I like Cheap," I said. "And it's not seven, it's nine."

"Well, I wasn't counting those two things," he waved a disparaging hand in the direction of Cheap and Nasty, who were keeping well away from the ewe lambs, just in case Henry should suddenly materialise again in the middle of them.

The new sheep with their black faces and woolly-fringed foreheads were Oxford Downs, he told me. Apparently they all had excellent pedigrees; and he had high hopes of doing well with them at agricultural shows...especially Henry.

In the face of Gerald's enthusiasm, I couldn't sustain my feeling of outrage at having had these extra animals delivered into my care without prior consultation; after all the little ewe lambs with their curly fringes were rather sweet.

He was so attentive and kind to me that evening, I knew he was relieved that I was taking my promotion to full shepherd with such good grace. As he said, I wouldn't really need to do anything with them, apart from keeping an eye on them during the day. Any of the more important or heavy jobs, he would do at the weekends. I really wanted to believe him.

Two days later, after he had done his early morning check of our livestock with binoculars from the step outside the scullery door, he came back into the kitchen for his brief case, and asked me to remove a long bramble which was stuck to Henry's wool.

Most farmers, I thought, would have pulled it off themselves, but then most farmers don't go to work in smart suits and highly polished shoes.

I finished my mug of coffee and removed my bottom from the Aga oven. After a ten-minute search I found the secateurs, which I didn't remember leaving in the bathroom, and went down to Henry's field.

It was empty.

Exit through three sides of it was impossible and, as I gazed along the line of the stream, I realised that half the stakes holding the electric fence had disappeared.

Running over to the clicking 'Electric Shepherd' I switched him off, then followed a trail of crushed vegetation along the stream bank, picturing the scene. Henry, his bramble caught on the electric fence, and maddened by the shocks pulsing through him, had stampeded through the undergrowth, and must have escaped over the stream.

I was wrong about him escaping. As I pushed my way through the brambles and stinging nettles, I found him; lying horribly still in two feet of water, under the drooping branches of an old willow tree, his wool lifting gently with the motion of the stream flowing over and round him. The electric fence wire was wound tightly round his body and legs.

Flinging myself into the stream, I managed to untangle enough of the wire to drag his front end onto the bank. He was heavier than he looked. A dead weight, in fact. He wasn't breathing. I thumped his chest near where I supposed his heart to be.

Nothing happened.

Gerald was going to be very upset, after all the

plans he'd had for Henry and his future progeny. His prize ram was dead and it was all my fault...if I had put the secateurs away in their proper place, Henry might still be alive.

In a last futile attempt, I sat on his chest and bounced up and down swearing... he coughed and some water dribbled from his mouth. I redoubled my efforts, as the water from his saturated wool soaked through my trousers, shouting encouragement to him. Then, as he coughed again, I untangled the rest of the wire and pulled him further up the bank.

He retched, coughed, and began to breathe properly and relief swept over me, suddenly tempered as I wondered whether he had been dead long enough to suffer brain damage. And how would one tell?

I pushed him to his feet, where he swayed groggily, a muddy mess with stinging nettles and twigs woven into his dripping fleece from his terrified attempts to escape the 'Electric Shepherd'.

A few more pushes got him back into the field, where he walked a step or two unaided, then lay down in the sunshine. I could clean him up later...meanwhile I thought we could both celebrate his return to life with a small brandy. I took mine neat but Henry's was laced with glucose and warm water.

I fed the rest of the animals, then spent the remainder of the morning untangling the electric fence, and trying to find the little black insulating things which fixed it to the stakes. These had 'pinged' off all over the field during Henry's struggles.

On the way back to the house, I stopped to check the other sheep. Nasty was amusing herself by beating up the ewe lambs. I shouted at her, and she left them and went back to her next favourite occupation, of uprooting our newly planted cupressus hedge along the boundary with the Barrington-Smythes. Cheap came over for a cuddle.

"Lovely day," he said, "especially now Henry's dead."

"He's only a bit dead, my love," I told him, marvelling that I could feel this much affection for a sheep.

It was becoming fairly obvious to me that I was never going to make a real shepherd. For a start, I had never seen a real shepherd kissing his sheep.

I telephoned Gerald to tell him about my rescue of Henry, but Hazel said he'd taken a client out to lunch, and did I want to leave a message. Not knowing quite where to start my message, I told her not to worry. It wasn't important. I still had a need to share my adventure with someone, so I phoned Erica.

"Whatever does he want sheep for? Do you want me to come over and have a look at the ram?" she offered.

"Only if you're still feeling bored."

Erica arrived with a bottle of wine - she thought I sounded a little stressed on the phone. She had a look at Henry who was now grazing normally, well away from the electric fence, and said he looked all right to her and where was the corkscrew.

What with the brandy, and having forgotten breakfast and lunch in the excitement, my stress fell away rapidly, leaving me so relaxed that I found it necessary to slump into an armchair and gossip the afternoon away with her.

"Why does Gerald need all these animals?" she asked.

"He doesn't need them, it's his hobby, like the wood-turning was."

She giggled at the memory of the pepper mills.

The wood-turning hadn't lasted very long, I reminded her, and I didn't think the farming would survive the next cold muddy winter.

"But he's not going to be doing it...he'll be in London," she pointed out.

I didn't want to have to think that far ahead; in fact I was fighting a strong desire to go to sleep.

"You'd better eat something," Erica said, making me a sandwich before she left.

When Gerald came home he was horrified at the state of Henry's fleece, which I had forgotten to clean up, and was none too happy about the fact that I hadn't called the vet out.

"He's all right. Erica came over and had a look at him."

"Oh, that's why there are brandy and wine glasses all over the place."

"That's an exaggeration. There are two wine glasses and the brandy was for Henry."

"Not my Remy Martin," he wailed.

"I saved the life of your prize ram Gerald...next time I'll let him drown," I sobbed, still somewhat under the influence of mixing the grain and the grape. What was happening to the man I had married not that long ago? Then he had seemed so easy going and we had shared the same sense of humour, but recently he seemed to have become much more short-tempered and intolerant.

Perhaps he was jealous because I seemed to be doing this latest hobby for him, but at that moment I was feeling too muzzy to think this theory through.

"Come on...stop snivelling. I'll take you down to the pub for supper," he said. "And thank you for rescuing Henry."

CHAPTER EIGHT

Henry didn't seem to have suffered from being drowned, and was soon back to his old macho self, though I noticed that he never grazed along the stream boundary after his accident.

As time went by, it was noticeable that the subject of tractor driving was being carefully avoided by Gerald, which suited me very well, as I had no intention of ever learning how to, and the brochure advertising the course was still buried under paperwork at the bottom of the desk drawer. So it was slightly embarrassing for both of us when Max came down for the weekend.

The first thing he said was: "Ooh! Can I have a go on the tractor?" He hadn't even got out of his car. Neither of us told him that even Gerald hadn't had a go on the tractor yet.

The car was the real reason for Max's visit, a gleaming red convertible sports car which he was driving with the hood down, in spite of the chilly weather. It suited him as he posed briefly, one elbow resting casually on the top of the door, before getting out.

Max is six feet tall and athletically built. With his dark brown hair and hazel eyes I think he's very handsome, but then I'm biased. Girls always seem to be swooning around him, but today he had come alone to show us the car, and see the alterations we had made to the house.

We admired his car and moved him away from the

vicinity of the tractor, to the house.

As we were drinking coffee in the kitchen, another car drew up in the yard. Max, who was standing near the window, paused with the coffee mug halfway to his mouth and said: "Cor! Look at that! Maybe the countryside isn't so bad."

Gerald got up and looked. "It's Sam; one of the Primroses is bulling again."

I must have missed this latest turn of events whilst taking the dogs for an early walk; a distant haze of yellow had attracted me up onto the common, where the blooming gorse dropped clouds of coconut scented sweetness around me as I strolled along the deserted sandy tracks.

"I've rung Ernie," Gerald said.

"Who's Ernie?" I asked.

"Ernie Challen."

Max was on his feet. "Shall I ask her in for coffee, Mum?"

"Why not."

The three dogs welcomed Sam like an old friend; they never forget a chocolate biscuit. She came in looking slightly bemused, but not swooning. She was too sensible for that, I decided. Max began asking Sam what her job entailed, and she grinned and gave him a detailed description of the introduction of bull's semen to a cow's uterus.

"D'you want to come and help?" she asked him, trying to hide a grin as he pushed a plate of chocolate cake to one side.

He looked down at his suede desert boots and cream jeans, his smile fading.

"Only teasing," she said, following his glance. "That's definitely not the gear for standing behind cows in."

Nevertheless, Max borrowed a pair of Gerald's wellingtons, and went with them when Mr Challen arrived a few minutes later.

The experience didn't seem to put him off Sam. They came back into the kitchen together and Max said he wouldn't be long, he was just taking Sam down to the pub for a drink before lunch. She borrowed the bathroom for a wash and brush up, emerging from a quick encounter with soap and water, looking better than I did after half an hour of moisturiser, foundation creams, mascara, eyeliner, powder and lipstick.

Ernie pocketed some money Gerald handed him, and rattled off up the track in his battered old white pick-up truck; the dog was in the back but separated from Gerald by a rope netting cover.

Gerald glared at it and it crouched down, but didn't take its eyes off him. He came in.

"Let's hope that's it and they're both in calf now' Sam thinks the other one has probably taken, but we'll have to get the vet to confirm it. She says we really should have a cattle crush to hold them still for the A.I. and veterinary examinations," he said.

I wondered why they called it a 'crush'. Cage would have sounded more humane.

Suddenly it sank in. Eventually the cows were going to give birth. They were bound to start doing it while I was on my own, and I hadn't a clue what to do. I wondered whether Sam could get them out as well as put them in.

Max left on Sunday evening, having arranged to meet Sam in London the following weekend. They both had my complete blessing. The sooner she was in the family the better. She was a farmer's daughter and had been to agricultural college.

My hopes of relying on Sam for support were dashed the following day when I spoke to Max on the phone, and he told me that she was planning to spend a year impregnating cows in Kenya.

A few days later the phone rang, just as I came in from putting Nasty back in her field and walking the dogs. It was raining heavily and the wind was coming from the east, chilling the rain before driving it horizontally into my face.

Struggling out of muddy wellingtons and dropping my wet coat on the kitchen floor, I grabbed the phone... replacing it after a few minutes with a deep sense of foreboding, tinged with fear. I knew nothing about 'birthing' cows, but I had thought I might have some time to find out before the Primroses went into labour next year.

A glorious Devonshire accent had just informed me that two pregnant South Devon cows would be arriving the following morning. This was the first I had heard of it...another of Gerald's little surprises for me. I tried to ring him, but he was conveniently 'in a meeting'. This was getting silly.

Making a cup of coffee to warm my hands on, I sat by the inglenook fireplace where our new woodburner was glowing invitingly. In an attempt to escape from reality my mind began to plan a romantic novel set in sun-drenched Rome. The dogs settled themselves on the rug at my feet, steaming gently, and dropped into toe twitching dreams of rabbits.

A gust of wind spattered some heavy drops of rain against the window, and I looked up to see Nasty's angry face pressed against the glass, dribbling snot down the pane as she demanded chocolate cake. This was an unfortunate development from Max's visit where he had fed her with a slice in an effort to gain her confidence. What he had gained was her undivided attention and everlasting love. Chocolate cake is ambrosia to sheep.

As Nasty's efforts to attract my attention were trampling some newly planted shrubs, I got up to put her back behind bars, disturbing the dogs who were plainly finding country life more tiring than London. All I could offer Nasty was a bourbon biscuit, but this seemed quite acceptable. Rome seemed a million miles away as the cold rain trickled down the back of my neck.

That evening Gerald arrived home with a present for me. A book full of cow gestation tables and horrific pictures of mummified calves, calves with two heads, and calves hanging upside-down over gates to drain the birth fluids from their lungs.

I told him point blank that I couldn't cope with any more cows. He ignored my complaints about aching legs and mud and heavy wheelbarrows, as he explained that getting these two new cows would mean that we would actually have pure bred South Devon calves on the farm this year, instead of having to wait through two pregnancies with the Primroses.

"Can't they have their calves somewhere else and then come to us?" I pleaded.

"No," he said. "They have to be born here to qualify for the Warren Hanger affix on their pedigrees. Take a longer view, Jill," he continued in his 'reasonable' voice. "These calves will be the foundation stock of what I hope will be one of the finest herds in the country."

He assured me that he would be around to help with the calvings, even if it meant coming home from the office - and there would be vets available. He made it sound so easy. He even offered to carry hay down to the field for the cows in the evenings from now on, thereby halving my heavy bale-carting duties.

He did actually do this - twice - before discovering that it was a nuisance to have to change his clothes when he came home; and anyway, he said, half past seven was really far too late for feeding cattle. A job which other farmers did around three o'clock in the afternoon.

It was too late to stop the delivery of these new cows, which were practically on their way, and had already been paid for, though he went a bit coy when I asked how much they had cost, and I never really did get an answer.

"Where shall I put them when they arrive?" I asked.

"With the others, of course."

"What if they fight?"

"Cows don't fight." He seemed amused by the idea.

The following morning the wind had swung round to the west and the sun had come out. I decided that the new cows could go into an old calf pen, which Ernie Challen had thoughtfully left bedded down with about three hundred years' worth of filthy straw. Gerald could turn them out into the field himself, when he came home.

I started to muck out the pen... I couldn't let the lorry driver see it as it was. The litter was three feet deep, soaking wet and the smell was indescribable; but I found I had set myself a task that would have taken even Hercules until after tea time. Deciding that the instincts of a housewife were not relevant to the farmyard, I followed my predecessor's example and spread clean straw on top of the noxious swamp.

Gerald rang to say he was taking a client to lunch and wouldn't be available again until around four o'clock, when I could advise him of the cows' arrival.

I toyed with the idea of lunch but the smell from my reeking jeans rose around me and removed any appetite I might have had.

The dogs, who had been helping me muck out, were also reeking but to them it was Chanel's best. I bathed them and turned them loose to dry in the sun, where they took turns at rolling on a dead mole, desperately trying to mask the smell of shampoo.

Just after lunch the cattle truck arrived. The driver glanced at me and asked if the boss was about. I told him there was only me there so I supposed I was the boss. He looked at a grubby clipboard.

"It says Gerald Collins here."

"That's my husband," I informed him, and invited him to take his lorry round the barn, and back it up to the sort of funnel I had built to direct the cows into their pen.

He gave me a very dubious look. "Perhaps we'd better wait for the guv'nor. Will he be long?"

Deciding he couldn't wait until seven o'clock, he reluctantly backed the lorry round the barn, lowered the rear ramp and opened the internal gates.

A giant ginger hippopotamus tiptoed carefully down the ramp, and gazed in a bemused fashion into my eyes. I returned the bemused stare with added horror. It was twice the size of the Primroses. The driver shooed it into the pen and went back to the lorry.

"There are supposed to be two," I said.

"There are," came a muffled voice from inside. "Goo on, gal!"

Silence.... "Goo on, old gal!"

More silence while the 'old gal' didn't 'goo on'.

"She don't seem to want to move," he said and suggested we "give 'er a minute".

We waited. The 'old gal' waited. The ginger hippopotamus waited. A heavy silence hung over the farm.

Into this silence came the 'trip trap, trip trap' of little cloven hoofs on the concrete. Nasty had escaped again. She shouldered aside the end of my funnel and marched up the ramp into the lorry. A second later she erupted out and disappeared at speed round the barn.

The lorry rocked on its springs, there was a loud bang from inside, a strangled shout, and the 'old gal' crashed-landed halfway down the ramp, slipped awkwardly off the side, and headed for her friend.

For a moment there was complete silence, then some strong agricultural language from inside the lorry, followed by: "What was that?"

"That was Nasty," I told him.

"Bloody near fatal," he said as he appeared at the top of the ramp wiping cow muck off his knees with a handful of straw.

He'd only had a glimpse of Nasty and thought she was a dog, until I explained, at which point he expressed the view that the sooner she was on a plate and covered with mint sauce, the better.

We tied up the gate of the cows' temporary home with some baler twine, as Ernie seemed to have mislaid the gate latch - probably used it to mend his tractor.

The lorry driver refused my offer of a drink and sandwich, as he had to get back to Devon that night, ready to take another load of cattle to market the following morning. Handing me a crumpled, grubby envelope he closed up the ramp on the lorry, and trundled away up the drive, pausing to lean on his horn to remove Nasty from his path. Clattering over the cattle grid he turned left, towards Devon, and the farm was quiet once more. Nasty returned to lie down again on the warm tarmac drive and I didn't have the heart to move her.

I opened the envelope to find two more registration certificates with the name Primrose on them, and wondered how many we would need for a bunch.

It was time for the afternoon feeds, which I had barely finished when Gerald arrived home early to see his new purchases.

"They're both called Primrose too," I told him.

"Mmm, aren't they gorgeous," he said.

"Can't we call them something else? Like Daisy and Buttercup," I asked. "All these Primroses are going to get very confusing."

"I'll just change and turn them out with the others," he said. "It's not confusing; these two are numbered 58 and 62."

I tried to remember the numbers of the other Primroses but couldn't, and decided we were in for some pretty complicated conversations about the Warren Hanger herd in future. Leaving Gerald to deal with the cows, I got on with preparing supper. After all the strenuous mucking out in the morning my arms were strangely weak, and water-filled saucepans seemed abnormally heavy. The potatoes were almost cooked when I glanced at the clock. Gerald had been gone for so long that I began to worry. Moving the pans off the heat, I went out to see what he was doing.

I could hear him shouting from the top yard, and from halfway down the hill could see him running around in the middle of the field, trying to keep the juggernauts apart. They, it seemed, were quite determined to establish a pecking order before settling to graze.

"Who says cow's don't fight?" I yelled from behind the gate.

"What? Ouch!" Gerald just escaped being sandwiched between two bovine brows as they cracked together. "They don't seem to like each other much," he shouted, obviously shaken.

The Ginger Hippopotamus and an original Primrose collided with a crack that echoed round the valley. Gerald yelled at them to stop.

"Olé...can I fetch your cape, Senor?" I called from the protection of my five-barred barrera, but he seemed to have lost his sense of humour.

"Stop making stupid remarks and come and give me a hand," he shouted, jerkily, as he thwarted another charge, this time from the Primrose with the shortened tail tassel; who, being pregnant, should have known better.

While I was pondering the sagacity of accepting his invitation, the cows suddenly forgot why they were fighting and began to graze.

Shame really, I was just beginning to enjoy the cows.

For a while Gerald treated them with a certain amount of respect, and thoughtfully warned me to be careful when entering the field to feed them.

The irony of this advice did not seem to register with him. The feeling I had once had of being cherished by him was rapidly disappearing. In fact, I was finding it hard to remember the last time I had felt cherished. Perhaps it was when Steve had made me a coffee after Nasty had knocked me off the haystack.

CHAPTER NINE

The cows quickly settled down together and became a docile herd. Though this made it easy to handle them, they were very boring - I much preferred the sheep. Even Henry was game for the occasional hug, though he would never take the place of Cheap in my affections.

The occasional sunny days were well outnumbered by wet, cold ones, and after a day of trudging through the mud I would find myself longing for pavements and ordinary shoes. The constant wearing of wellingtons was rubbing a sore patch on the inside of my calves, and summer couldn't come soon enough.

I complained again to Gerald about having to carry hay for the cows, and he decided to move a week's supply of bales down to just outside their field gate, and cover them with a tarpaulin to keep them dry.

It was probably a disinclination to do this by hand that forced him into a closer relationship with the tractor, but he picked a bad day for his first practice run.

It had rained steadily for most of the week and the ground was sodden. By Saturday it was still drizzly, though beginning to clear as the prevailing west wind started to veer round to the east. He waited until I, unaware of his plans, had left for the town to pick up a few things which the village store didn't stock, then mounted his steed.

Not only was it a bad day because of the slippery conditions, but what neither of us had realised was that

77

the Barrington-Smythes had returned to their cottage late the previous night.

When I arrived home the accident had only just happened. Apparently Gerald had driven up and down the drive a few times without mishap then, becoming more adventurous, had decided to cart a water trough across the dog paddock, using the box on the back of the tractor. My complaints about having to carry buckets of water out to the sheep had finally got through to him.

The flock had been grazing quietly until Gerald trundled in and startled them. He managed to get off the tractor and shut the gate just before they escaped, then drove across the paddock to the water supply near the boundary with the Barrington-Smythes.

He swears it was Nasty's fault. Apparently she made a panicky dive for the tractor and he had to swerve to avoid her; the soggy ground dissolved under the tractor tyres, sending it sliding through our baby cupressus hedge, and into the chain link fence between the field and the Barrington-Smythes' garden. The fence snapped and buckled, bringing down two of the posts.

Nasty seized her chance to escape from the monster she was convinced was chasing her, and took Cheap and the six ewe lambs with her into the immaculate garden.

The revving of the tractor engine caught my attention as I got out of the car, and I could see the sheep streaming through the gap in the fence. I grabbed Cheap's halter from just inside the stable door, and ran across the paddock. After a few grinding noises Gerald managed to find reverse gear and back the tractor off the fence.

The sheep spread out in the cottage garden. A lamb

collided with a terracotta flowerpot on the patio, spilling plants and compost onto the flagstones; and a narrow rustic arch swayed alarmingly as Cheap and three lambs tried to get through it in line abreast.

A shriek from inside the cottage alerted us to the fact that we were not alone, then Lavinia Barrington-Smythe appeared, and started stabbing at the ewe lambs with the metal point of a shooting stick, whilst calling Gerald a "bloody fool". At this rate, I thought, he's going to go off her just as quickly as he'd fallen for her in the pub.

As the rustic arch finally collapsed sideways in slow motion, he tried to apologise to the now nearly hysterical Lavinia, but she didn't give him a chance, and let loose a stream of quite shocking language, interspersed with remarks about incompetent idiots who played at farming, as she disappeared round the cottage after the ewe lambs who were making for the kitchen garden and the hitherto-unknown delights of cabbage.

"Bloody woman!" said Gerald as I passed him, and climbed through the crushed fence.

If I could just catch Cheap, who was now standing on the lawn looking worried, there was a chance I could lead the others out. But as I approached him he backed away, and slipped into the ornamental pond behind him.

Lavinia was still round at the back of the cottage, shouting at the lambs, as I flung myself into the pond, from where, with me pushing and him scrabbling, Cheap managed to extricate himself. As he stood on the edge and shook himself like a dog, a rather flat Koi carp rose slowly to the surface, and floated there amongst the uprooted water lilies.

I put his halter on and managed to attract Nasty and the lambs back into the paddock, apologising over my shoulder to Lavinia, who was still hitting any lamb she could reach with the shooting stick. I led the flock straight across and out of the paddock, leaving Gerald to deal with her.

She would have none of his apologies, and stormed indoors screeching that her husband would deal with him when he came home.

"Woman's insane," said Gerald as he walked in, having made a temporary repair to the fence. "There was no serious damage that couldn't be sorted out with a rake and a few new plants."

"Cheap killed one of their fish," I said, struggling out of my soaking jeans in front of the Aga - and we both had hysterics.

Piers Barrington-Smythe didn't tackle Gerald directly, but we received a hefty bill for repairs to the garden. Gerald paid this, and would have tried to heal the rift which had developed between us, but they gave him no opening, and slowly a range war developed.

It began one quiet Sunday morning with an invasion. We looked up from our breakfast to see Lavinia, the two children, and their supercilious grandmother, march aggressively past our kitchen window, trailing what appeared to be a brain-dead labrador on the end of a lead.

"What the hell?" said Gerald. We watched them as they went up the drive and turned towards the village. He made a dive for the desk drawer which held the plans of the farm.

"They've found the footpath," he said.

The footpath ran through the wood, along behind the Barrington-Smythes' cottage, over a crumbling stile, well overgrown by a hawthorn hedge, and through one of our fields. Then the plans clearly showed it leading straight across our back yard, six feet from the kitchen window, and up the drive to the road.

Ernie Challen had long ago thrown the footpath signs away, and trained a nice crop of brambles and stinging nettles over the path, and it had fallen out of sight and out of use. He'd said nobody had used it for about twenty years.

The Barrington-Smythes had a perfectly good drive of their own up to the road, which only added a hundred yards to their journey to the village, but they now chose to march through our garden.

Having discovered the footpath, it became a sort of crusade with Lavinia to keep it open. She didn't quite reach the stage of carrying a corpse to the churchyard over it - grandmother still looked pretty fit - but she did seem to be marshalling some kind of an army on her side, because gradually the traffic built up.

Several times a day on Saturdays and Sundays, jolly bearded walkers with their earnest-looking mates, maps in plastic covers dangling from strings round their necks, would tramp past the kitchen window smiling and waving at whoever was at the sink.

'Apoplectic' was the word which sprang to mind when watching Gerald on these occasions, he was developing a severe 'Git orf moi land' complex, and I began to dread the weekends and long for Mondays.

He tried to get me to speak to Lavinia 'woman to woman', but in spite of my newfound self confidence in handling enormous cows and crazy sheep, I was experiencing difficulty in screwing my courage up to the point of tackling a woman who had such a demoralising effect on a perfectly innocuous labrador. Besides, over the use of the footpath, she was technically correct and had a map to prove it. It seemed the lesser of two evils to keep waving and smiling across the sink, like royalty, every weekend.

My lack of obvious support drove Gerald to more desperate measures. He encouraged the dogs to bark continuously through the paddock fence when the Barrington-Smythes were in their garden. The dogs found this huge fun and turned sullen when I brought them in. Piers threatened Gerald with the noise abatement society.

Then, when the field had dried out, Gerald drove the tractor across to the now-repaired fence and left it parked with the engine running, puffing out noxious diesel particulates across their patio. The tractor ran out of fuel, and draining the last few filthy dregs from its tank made it very unhappy, necessitating professional repair.

The escalating hostilities took a definite turn for the physically dangerous the weekend after this episode.

With the fence mended, the sheep were back in the dog paddock, and as I crossed the dining room, I glanced out of the window to see them acting in a most peculiar manner, grazing quietly one moment, then suddenly galloping across the paddock to stand twitching and shaking their ears by the gate.

Calling Gerald, I went out for a closer look and noticed some strange dark shapes lurking behind the fence in the Barrington-Smythes garden. Crossing the paddock to investigate, I realised the shapes were emitting an angry humming sound.

They were beehives! Lavinia had taken up beekeeping, and these bees were not happy in their new home. I wondered if she'd had to search far to find a strain which appeared to be closely related to the African Killer bee.

Cheap went thundering past me, having obviously just been stung, and I ran to fetch his halter to lead him and the rest of the flock to safety. Gerald went over to see for himself, and got stung three times in as many seconds. He stamped indoors to phone the Barrington-Smythes, while I took the sheep to the other end of the farm and turned them in with the cows.

The sheep couldn't decide which was worse, bees or cows, and huddled miserably in a corner of the field as far from the Primroses as they could get.

When I got back indoors I shut all the windows, before reading the note Gerald had left me. There had been no answer to his phone call, and he had gone up to the village shop, to see if Margaret had some soda to treat his stings.

In the shop he gleaned the information that Lavinia had only borrowed the hives from someone in the next village. He also found out that bees are not supposed to be placed less than a certain distance from a neighbour's boundary, and the siting of Lavinia's hives was definitely illegal.

He telephoned the beekeeper, who hadn't realised that the paddock was our property, and had put the hives where Lavinia had told him. He was most apologetic and came straight over to move them to the other side of her garden.

About a week later he came and removed them altogether; after one of the children had been stung, so Margaret told me.

The sheep were returned to the paddock, and we found that we had benefited from the killer bee episode, in that the sheep would no longer graze along the boundary fence, with the consequence that the cupressus hedge began to grow nicely, freed from

Nasty's depredations.

We willed the hedge to grow thick and fast, and above all, high.

"About fifteen feet high," Gerald said, as he spread a foul-smelling fertilizer along its base. His aim was to remove the sun from their patio for most of the year.

The situation gradually improved: the children returned to their boarding schools, and Piers and Lavinia went back to Hong Kong.

Walkers, tired of being scratched by brambles and stung by nettles, and lacking the incentive of Lavinia's urging, gradually ceased to use the footpath, finding the slightly longer journey by road much more comfortable. The nettles grew back and peace was restored.

Gerald decided to leave any serious tractor driving until the mud had dried up a bit, and carted some hay down to the cows field for me using the wheelbarrow, but this small supply was soon eaten and the job was once more delegated to me.

CHAPTER TEN

Sunshine was pouring through the bedroom window, and a blackbird was singing in the apple tree at the bottom of the back garden. I leaned on the window ledge, drinking in the view of the wooded hillside and the common beyond, where the silver birches were just breaking into pale green leaf, their trunks gleaming white as the rising sun lit them from underneath.

"It's a beautiful day," I told Gerald, who grunted and muttered something about tea before sinking back into sleep.

Smoke was drifting lazily into the air from a bonfire on the far side of the wood, and the distant buzz of a chain saw conjured a picture of Conor, clearing away the oak tree which the last gale had brought down across the fence, between the wood and common.

Those incredible blue eyes would be concentrating on the saw cutting into the hard wood, skilfully manipulated by his strong brown arms.

I reminded myself that I didn't like Conor.

Quickly pulling on jeans and a shirt, I left the bedroom, then went back for a jersey. It might look beautiful out there but I had been cold for so long I didn't really trust the weather; the Downs in the distance were too sharp and clear. Even the white walls of Telegraph House, standing on the highest point, were visible today. All this clarity was a sure sign of rain later.

The dogs were eager to be out in the sun, and shot

out of the door into the garden in full cry, just in case there was a squirrel on the lawn. There had been once, and they had never forgotten it. Neither had the squirrel, because it hadn't been back. The blackbird gave an alarm call and flew off to continue his song in the oak tree by the stream.

I put a cup of tea on the bedside table beside Gerald's unconscious body, and took mine out into the back garden overlooking the field, which sloped down to the stream before rising slightly on the other side of a narrow stone bridge. Our small flock of sheep was lying on this gentle rise to the wood, enjoying the sunshine, steam rising from their dew-damp wool.

My contemplation of this bucolic idyll was interrupted by a voice from the dormer window above me.

"It's too nice to lie in bed. Shall we have an early breakfast?"

This meant...I'm getting up now, so if you start breakfast it should be ready when I am.

A breeze had sprung up, and a few white fluffy clouds dotted the horizon as I went indoors and took bacon and eggs from the fridge.

Half an hour later an odd sound from the kitchen window interrupted Gerald's concentration, which was equally divided between the newspaper and his full English breakfast, a weekend luxury.

We turned to see thick green slime running down the outside of the glass.

"What on earth's that?" he choked.

"The Martians have landed?" I suggested, joining him at the window.

The sun was now hidden by a dark bank of cloud drifting across it. Outside, on the cobbled yard, stood

Nasty, her eyes fixed on the back door; then she saw us at the window and demanded chocolate cake.

Gerald pointed to the slime. "How did she do that?"

At that moment a glistening green fountain erupted from the corner of the house, and splattered onto the cobbles, followed by a staggering, and obviously very ill, Cheap. He heaved, opened his mouth and deposited another green pool. Nasty studied him dispassionately for a second, before returning to her chocolate cake vigil.

As we rushed outside the rest of our small flock appeared round the corner, and I realised that 'my bloody ewe' had surpassed herself this morning by letting them all out.

It didn't take long to establish the cause of Cheap's misery. Two dwarf azaleas we had planted in a new flowerbed along the barn wall had been reduced to a few bare twigs. This was serious, I recalled reading somewhere that azaleas were poisonous to goats, and therefore probably to sheep as well.

I dashed indoors to phone the vet, while Gerald herded the rest of the sheep back to their field; hindered by the dachshunds who thought they were auditioning for 'One Man and his Dog'.

"Azalea poisoning?" said the vet. "Nothing much I can do about it. He'll probably die. How much has he eaten?"

Die?... Cheap couldn't die... I loved him. He was my friend. He loved being cuddled, and was an interested listener to all my troubles when I needed a sympathetic ear, albeit a furry one.

Half my mind had gone into shock...the other half was reeling at the callous attitude of these farm vets. Our previous vet in London would have had Cheap rushed into hospital and put on a drip.

"Two bushes," I said.

"That's fairly precise."

How could he mock at a time like this? I described as best I could the amount of poisonous greenery that Cheap had ingested, and the vet asked if he was a valuable pedigree ram.

What did that have to do with anything?

My foolish admission that he was a wether I used for grass mowing, brought a repeat of the information that he would probably die, and when I pressed him for some hope and help, he offered to come and put Cheap out of his misery - an offer which I declined.

Gerald had put the other sheep away but Cheap and Nasty were still by the back door; Cheap dying dramatically, and Nasty complaining that she would very likely join him if she didn't soon get some cake. The first few drops of rain were plopping onto the cobbles.

"What did the vet say?" Gerald asked, as he came in to finish his breakfast. He knew there was no point in trying to put Nasty back into the field before she was ready to go.

I told him the vet only cured pedigree sheep, which seemed reasonable to Gerald; then I wept for a minute, which put him off his food to the extent that he offered to put Cheap back in the field, so that he "could die with his friends around him."

With hindsight it may not have been my weeping which had dulled his appetite; it was more likely the strangled gurgling and choking coming from outside the kitchen window.

We half carried the staggering Cheap back to his field, with Nasty wandering along behind us, sulking because I had only given her a piece of cold toast. Just inside the gate Cheap collapsed with a groan, and Gerald suggested we leave him in peace, which I translated as 'I don't like watching sheep die'.

By lunchtime Cheap had stopped being sick, and was giving a very good impression of a ewe in the final stages of a difficult labour. Unable to watch my friend suffer any more, I drove into town to the vet's surgery to see if there was any treatment at all that he could offer for Cheap's agonising stomach cramps.

He was surprised to hear that he was still alive, and gave me a hypodermic syringe full of a spasmolytic drug, with the instruction that I was to 'stick it in Cheap's backside'!

As I started to explain that I was in no way qualified to administer injections, his phone rang, and he wished me luck as he turned to answer it.

I raced home, trying to drive both fast and safely along the slippery twisting lanes, windscreen wipers working at top speed. As I slowed down to turn into the drive, I glanced at the syringe lying beside my handbag on the passenger seat, and cursed the fact that the only nurse I knew really well, lived in London - but even she wasn't used to giving injections whilst kneeling in a patch of stinging nettles in the rain.

The squeal of tyres as I drew up in the yard startled Gerald who was leaning on the field gate looking at the still white mound just inside it. He put his arm round my shoulders as he said: "I'm sorry darling, he died about five minutes ago."

Torn between grief, and relief that I wouldn't have to stab him with the syringe, I knelt beside my old friend who opened one eye and groaned.

Gerald nearly became a blood donor once, but

fainted at the advance of the first needle, so I knew I was on my own.

He turned grey as he watched me pull the cover off the huge needle on the syringe.

"Don't you dare faint," I told him as I knelt beside Cheap and parted the wool on his backside. Gritting my teeth, and taking a deep breath, I pushed the needle into the exposed pink flesh, and pressed home the plunger. Cheap didn't move but Gerald swayed, hanging onto the gate with one hand, unconscious of the fact that he was rubbing his bottom with the other.

Giving injections is very stressful, and I found that once I had got indoors, I was shaking. Gerald poured brandies for both of us. Two glasses later I staggered groggily down to check on my patient. It was a miracle. Cheap was up on his feet and staggering, equally groggily, around the field.

Putting my arm round his neck, I bent down to give him a kiss, and we both fell over. But it didn't matter. Cheap was going to live, and the sun was coming out again.

CHAPTER ELEVEN

Cheap's health improved but the weather did not, and it was beginning to feel as if spring would never arrive. Winds straight from Siberia were freezing the puddles in the yard, and driving horizontal flurries of stinging sleet into any face stupid enough to be out in it.

The Primroses huddled together in the more sheltered parts of their field, with their backs to the wind and heads lowered. The sheep weren't unduly bothered but then they were dressed for it. All of the animals became hungrier though, and tending to Gerald's latest hobby ceased to be even remotely amusing, and turned into daily drudgery.

It had been hard enough to push the wheelbarrow loaded with hay through the mud, but now that the ruts had frozen solid it was even more difficult, and I finally resorted to carrying the bales by hand. As I could only manage one at a time, this doubled the time spent feeding the cows at the bottom of the hill. We had run out of the hay which Mr Challen had left us down in the bottom barn, and for some reason Gerald had got the chap who delivered the next load, while I was out, to stack it in the barn in the top yard.

Carrying food to the sheep was not such a heavy job, but infinitely more dangerous. They had a long galvanised iron trough in their field into which I had to pour a bucket of sheep nuts, a sort of compressed cereal feed which they loved. In an ideal situation, the nuts would be spread along the length of the trough to allow equal shares for all. In reality, doing the job properly was impossible. I took my life in my hands every day as soon as I got through the field gate. Even this was not easy as they were all leaning against it from the other side, trying to reach the bucket as I struggled with the latch. Once through the gate I had to race them to the trough, and run along it pouring out their food.

I rarely managed to reach the end before either a head had dived into the bucket, and knocked it out of my hand, or worse, a head had dived between my legs to reach the trough, pinning me onto the shoulders of a greedily guzzling sheep, who was hardly aware that I was there. It is extremely difficult to slide off thick wool, which has great clinging properties, and I had collected more than my fair share of bruises, before it occurred to me to throw some sheep nuts onto the ground just inside the gate on my way in, which delayed them somewhat.

"He doesn't realise just what he has lumbered you with," Erica had said. "You'll have to speak to him; he doesn't understand just how exhausting that kind of work can be for a woman of your age."

Now I know Erica is nine years younger than me, but I wasn't sure this was the kind of commiseration I wanted to hear. But it did firm my resolve to tackle Gerald again, and try to persuade him that farming was not a good idea for us, until he could follow Derek's example and retire; then he could do it properly.

"Can I talk to you about this farming thing?" I said to the top of his head one evening, as he read his paper whilst eating supper.

"Mmm." He didn't look up.

Somehow the reasoned arguments, which I had been practising over peeling the potatoes, flew out of my head and I found myself whining: "I don't want to be a farmer, Gerald, look at my hands, they're ruined. I'm getting tired of being cold and wet...and I'm tired of being tired. It's all right for you in your nice warm office, but this is silly, we don't need all these animals, and my legs ache."

"You're just tired, darling." He was still reading the paper.

"Tired! I know I'm bloody tired; haven't you been listening?"

As my voice rose, he looked up.

"It's the carrying, isn't it? I'll teach you to drive the tractor."

"If my parents were still alive I'd be tempted to go home to my mother...what do you mean, you'll teach me to drive the tractor? Your record in that department hardly qualifies you as an instructor."

He winced.

Then using Erica's argument - because it was all right for me to do so - I told him I was far to old to start trying to drive a tractor around a steep muddy farm. I had recently found it hard enough trying to keep the car from skidding off the tarmac lane to the village, since the neighbouring farmer had started 'leek lifting'. Transporting his crop from the field had involved dropping tons of mud on the road from his tractor tyres, and the only warning of this hazard was a triangular sign with an exclamation mark on it... or was it a leek dropping a clod of earth?

Gerald had gone across to the desk.

"There was a brochure here somewhere," he said, searching through the drawers. Then he gave up. "It was from Brinsbury Agricultural College. They do a tractor-driving course for farmers' wives. I could book you on the next one...then you could teach me."

He laughed. I didn't.

I told him what he could do with Brinsbury College and his Fergie, and he said farming was coarsening me. But he did say he would have a word with Ernie Challen, to see if maybe he would put in a few hours each week to cope with the heavier jobs.

This wasn't what I had set out to achieve, but I wasn't about to turn down help from any quarter, and at least Ernie knew about farming.

The following day after struggling with the elements, and cold, uncooperative, animals, I staggered in as dusk fell, and collapsed on a chair in front of the Aga, trying to bring some feeling back to my fingers by holding them over the hotplate. Gerald wasn't due back for an hour and I needed to thaw out before starting to cook supper.

As the blood began to flow painfully back into my fingers, there was a sound behind me. I turned, to see the coat, which was hanging on the back of the kitchen door, swinging slightly. The door slowly creaked ajar, Huggy growled and I felt my eyes widen as they fixed on the muzzle of the gun sliding through the gap. Cold crept down the back of my head and neck as the hairs rose, and fear glued me to the chair.

I had been half expecting something awful like this - the farmhouse was so remote after our cosy London flat. I was completely alone... I screamed!

Gerald pushed the door open grinning, and put the gun down beside the dresser.

"It was a joke," he laughed.

"Joke!" I shrieked. "I could have had a heart attack! Have you any idea how scary it can be here sometimes, surrounded by mad rapists and the IRA? Where did you get that gun? And why are you early?"

"Don't be silly. There wasn't much on at work." He hugged me. "I'm sorry I frightened you. I got it from a chap I know on the train."

"Does British Rail know they are carrying armed bank managers?"

"I travel with him every day. It belonged to his son."

He went on to explain that no self-respecting farm should be without a 4.10. Picking it up again he broke it open, and as the dogs, already unnerved by my scream, quietly took refuge under the dresser, I realised they had done nothing to defend me from potential murder.

Whilst I was still recovering from facing my imminent death, Gerald dealt me another blow, by suggesting that it was about time we had his parents to stay for a few days.

My heart sank. Gerald's parents were still upset about the break-up of his first marriage, and although this had happened before I came on the scene, there was still an awkwardness between us.

Mary and Arnold were complete city dwellers; to them the countryside was something which happened at speed through car windows, and I knew the farm would be found wanting in paved areas and street lights.

Inspiration came rushing to the rescue.

"What about the rats?" I asked.

"Rats!" Gerald was horrified. He hadn't noticed any rats - this was probably because he rarely went out to the farmyard at night, taking after his mother where street lights were concerned. In fact, the barn opposite the house came alive after dark with rustles, thumps and squeaks, and nasty humpbacked shapes could be seen sneaking across the yard in the moonlight. The scene could have been incorporated into a Hammer House of Horror film.

"Well, we have the answer here," he said, picking up his new toy and removing a box of cartridges from his brief case. "I'll shoot them."

I mused for a moment on the effect that holding a gun had on him, and decided I didn't like it. My suggestion that we should poison the rats was countered by the fact that we might also poison the dogs. He wasn't going to lose a genuine opportunity to play with his gun.

The following day was an exhausting repeat of the one before, and I resolved to make sure Gerald phoned Ernie Challen when he came home and arranged for him to start work as soon as possible. Especially if I was going to have to entertain his parents for a few days. I couldn't expect them to wait around for most of the day while I looked after the animals. Mary was going to love all this, I thought, as I knocked five pounds of wet clay off each wellington boot outside the back door.

I didn't bother to rinse the boots under the outside tap; it was too cold, and after spending most of the day outside battling with the mud, and miserable shivering animals, I was ready for a little tender loving care myself, even if it did have to be self-administered nowadays.

I had only just collapsed in the chair beside the Aga with a strong coffee, trying to summon the energy to get me through the last feed of the day, Gerald's supper, when he arrived home, a gin and tonic from the train glowing gently inside him.

Without removing his coat he took his new gun out of the cupboard. "Right, come on," he said.

"Come on where?" I asked.

It turned out that he wanted me to go back out into the cold and hold the torch for him while he shot at the rats.

"Gerald, I intend to die in the fullness of time, when I'm called, and preferably in the warm...not freeze to death in the yard rat-spotting for you," I snapped.

"You're no fun any more," he said as he tied the torch to the gun barrel with one of the dog leads, and marched intrepidly out into the night.

One minute later he marched intrepidly back into the kitchen.

"Forgot these," he said, picking up the box of cartridges.

After ten minutes of sound effects worthy of the battle of the Somme, he entered the kitchen with a verbal fanfare.

"Ta Raaa!" and held up an enormous, mangy, grandfather rat by its horrible scaly tail.

The rat twitched and gave a feeble squeak. Instantly Huggy launched himself from the dog bed, and snatched the half-dead rodent from Gerald, shaking it violently, and spraying blood and rat urine all around the kitchen.

Gerald dived at Huggy, who disappeared under the dresser with his kill, and snarled menacingly at the groping hand which followed him. It was dark under the dresser and Gerald demanded the torch. There was momentary confusion as I asked where the gun was, and he protested that he didn't intend to shoot the rat under the dresser.

I gingerly untied the torch from the gun, which was propped up outside the back door, and having established Huggy's exact position, we dragged him and the rat out with a broom. The rat was very dead now and, apart from the fact that he didn't want Gerald to have it, Huggy had largely lost interest in it when it had ceased to move.

The phone rang. I went to answer it as Gerald took the rat outside to the dustbin. It was Jim, landlord of the 'Royal Oak', wondering if we had lost a sheep as there was one in his car park, begging for crisps from passing customers.

It just had to be Nasty.

Gerald vaguely remembered hearing some commotion when he began slaughtering rats. It had taken Nasty no time at all to appreciate the danger of Gerald, plus a 4.10.

We went out to the paddock and put the halter on Cheap, and set off with him to the pub. A half-mile walk along dark country lanes to the village was just what I needed to round off my day. We took Cheap to lure Nasty home, and I stuffed some bourbon biscuits in my pocket to make quite sure she would follow us.

By the time we arrived half an hour later, she had collected quite a fan club and was munching her way through a large slice of Black Forest Gâteau. Another slice was brought out for Cheap, by Jim's five-year-old daughter, Sarah. I was starving but didn't like to ask for some.

When Cheap had finished his, and was still licking the cream from his whiskery lips, I popped Sarah onto his warm woolly back, and gave her a ride round the car park. Cheap was a very accommodating animal; he seemed to enjoy it, so did most of the pub customers, who were now out in the freezing cold cheering her on.

Light, warmth, and a wonderful smell of food spilled out of the pub doorway, and I remembered that our kitchen was now contaminated with Weils disease, and probably bubonic plague, necessitating hours of cleaning and disinfecting. We arranged to go back and eat at the pub after we'd taken the sheep home.

One good thing which came out of 'The Night of the Rat', as it became known, was that Ernie was in the pub when we got back there, and he agreed to come and give us a hand on the farm.

It was quite some time before Cheap and Nasty came to terms with the fact that I was not going to provide Black Forest Gâteau as a regular constituent of their diet... and having proved that we did have a rat problem, Gerald decided that it would be better for his parents to come down later in the year - apparently rats migrate out of farm buildings into the countryside for the summer.

"Mum and Dad would love to give you a hand on the farm," he said.

I doubted it. Gerald's parents' closest brush with nature had been caring for a neighbour's budgerigar for a week, while its owner was on holiday, and they had sworn: "Never again...the MESS it made!"

Anyway, the rats had given me a welcome reprieve, it would be much easier to entertain his parents in the summer time.

CHAPTER TWELVE

Suddenly, whoever organises the weather relented; and as a miserable April moved towards May, spring seemed to be in the air at last. I looked out of the bedroom window one bright morning to see a fat baby bird sitting, hunched, on the garden wall. The yellow rim round its beak was turned down at the corners, giving it a very disgruntled expression as it sat glaring into the apple tree. Then it suddenly sprang shrieking, wing-flapping life, as a harassed robin, with a couple of tail feathers missing, landed on the wall two feet away, its beak full of squirming caterpillars. Instantly there was something odd about the scene...babies are supposed to be smaller than their parents, not twice as large. This one just had to be a cuckoo.

Would the cuckoo move towards the robin, thereby saving it a little of its obviously depleted energy? Of course not; this outrageous child just screeched its demands until the poor foster parent could stand it no longer and, hopping along the wall, jammed the wide mouth full of caterpillars.

Actually seeing a cuckoo for the first time should have been exciting, but I found myself disliking this baby. It was already a serial killer, having thrown the robins' eggs out of the nest; and now it had forced the bereaved parents into slave labour.

"What are you looking at?" asked Gerald, as he compared the time on the alarm clock with his watch.

"Bloody cuckoo," I said.

He got out of bed and joined me at the window.

"Why is it a 'bloody' cuckoo? Oh, how about that, it's only a baby. How can you not like a baby cuckoo?"

When I tried to describe my feelings about it, he explained that nature was red in tooth and claw, which suddenly struck me as a very easy cliché for people to trot out, so that they don't have to think about the nastier side of nature.

"Ernie's coming today," he said. "Get him to move that hay down to the bottom barn, and he can feed the animals as well. You have a day off and enjoy the sunshine."

After I had given Ernie his instructions, I decided to take the dogs for a long walk up onto the common, the other side of what I had come to think of as Conor's wood. I now kept the dogs on a lead through the wood, and stayed on the footpath, trying not to admit to myself that I was a little afraid of meeting an angry Conor in this lonely place.

Once on the common I released the dogs, who were instantly onto the scent of something and raced off ahead of me. I wandered along the dry sandy tracks, between sweeps of young heather and birch plantations, expecting the dogs to come back to me any minute.

I had still not quite come to terms with the fact that, though reasonably well behaved in a London park, three dachshunds in the country constitutes a hunting pack.

A deer paused for an instant on the skyline about quarter of a mile away, then disappeared; the faint music of my hounds in full cry drifted back to me.

I increased my pace. It looked as if the deer was running in a right-handed circle, which would take it into the far end of Conor's wood. I began to run after the dogs, whistling to them, until I found I needed all my breath for running.

By the time I caught up with them about ten minutes later, they had given up on the deer. When your legs are only four inches long, deer chasing is a pretty ambitious game. They had changed onto the scent of rabbits, and were now dashing about in a large rabbit warren, just inside the wood.

I climbed through the rickety post and rail fence, about two hundred yards from the fallen oak, from which Conor had stripped most of the smaller branches. A burnt area nearby showed where he had made the bonfire which had created the smoke I had seen.

Below the fence was a slippery ditch, lined with brambles; the dogs could hardly have chosen a more difficult entry point into the wood. When I had finally unhooked my jacket from a particularly vicious bramble on the other side of the ditch, I could see that Rudi was still above ground, and I managed to lasso him with a lead, much to his annoyance.

The tip of Huggy's tail was just visible, shaking with the effort he was putting into digging his way furiously into a burrow, earth spraying out behind him. Grabbing his tail, I pulled him out, and nearly got bitten before he realised it was me. That was two of them caught. I couldn't see or hear Flicka anywhere. Flicka is a very long, lean, smooth-haired silver dapple. She looks like a snake and slithers down rabbit holes with serpentine ease.

I knew I was going to have to wait for her to come out when she was ready. Huggy was lunging furiously at his collar in an attempt to get back to his hole, and the pressure on his throat gave him a fit of coughing. When he finally got his breath again he gave up, and lay panting at my feet with Rudi, while I sat on a handy log, ears finely tuned to any sound that would show Flicka's whereabouts.

After about half an hour with no sign of her at all, I began to wonder if she had come into the wood with the others, or was maybe still hunting the deer. I asked Huggy where she was, trying to get him to show me where she might have gone to ground, but he was no help. Every time we got near a hole he switched into rabbit-killing mode, with no thought for his girl friend.

An hour passed. Huggy and Rudi were fidgeting and I had things to do at home...perhaps Flicka was already there waiting for us...and maybe getting killed under the wheels of the tractor as Ernie moved the hay. As this thought struck me, I decided to go home.

She wasn't by the back door, and Ernie hadn't seen her.

"Your ewe's out though, she's down the bottom. I was just going to chase 'er back."

"Thanks, but you carry on with the hay. I'll get Nasty," I said.

She was standing beside the gate into Henry's field, nose to nose with the ram I thought she hated. Fickle things sheep; these two were obviously madly in love. So besotted was Nasty at that moment that she hardly noticed when I slipped a dog lead round her neck.

Then she did, and it was quite a struggle to get her back into the field with Cheap and the ewe lambs, who were getting bigger every day. Gerald was already calculating how soon he could turn Henry in with them and embark on his sheep-breeding programme.

I dashed through the jobs I had to do, listening for the squeak of the hinges on the scullery door, which I had left ajar for Flicka to push her way in. But the squeak didn't come.

By mid-day I was convinced that something awful had happened to her and, leaving the other dogs behind, I set off once more for the rabbit warren.

The wonderful morning had gone, and it was beginning to rain as I made my way through the wood, keeping a wary eye open for Conor. When I reached the warren I alternately called Flicka, then listened for some kind of answer from her, but the rain hitting the leaves of the oak trees around me made it impossible to hear other sounds.

Getting down on my hands and knees, I began calling down rabbit holes, then putting my ear to them and listening. After ten minutes of this I was soaked and covered in mud to my knees and elbows. At the sixth burrow I thought I heard something, and was lying full length in the mud with my arm down the hole, when a pair of boots appeared in front of my face. I looked up into those mesmerising blue eyes.

"Doing a bit of poaching?" asked Conor. He was trying hard not to laugh.

This was no time for embarrassment or pride; I needed help.

"I'm sorry, but I think one of my dogs is down here," I said weakly.

"Move over," he said, dropping to his knees beside me. I stood up quickly. Somehow, lying beside Conor in the mud would be far too intimate, and fraught with danger, though what danger I couldn't really fathom. I was flustered...why did this man always seem to catch me at a disadvantage? My hair was a wet bedraggled mess and I just knew that the rain would have smudged mascara down my cheeks.

Furthermore, I was convinced that it was his voice we had heard from the wood when we were trying to catch Henry, and that he probably thought Gerald and I, and our attempts at farming, were a great joke. I considered strangling Flicka, if we got her out alive.

He listened at the hole for some seconds, then agreed that he could hear her whining.

"Going to need a spade," he said. "Won't be long."

While he was gone I knelt at the hole, listening to the intermittent faint whines coming from deep underground, and trying to reassure Flicka that help was on the way. When he came back we alternated in our rescue attempt. He dug, then I lay on the ground with my arm as far down the hole as I could reach. The tunnel still seemed wide enough for Flicka to have come out as we got deeper in, and the whining became louder, then running my hand round the circumference of the tunnel, I felt a wet lump sticking down through the roof of the passage. As I touched it, it moved, and a tongue licked my hand.

"I can feel her nose; it's hanging down through the roof."

Relief that I could actually touch Flicka cancelled out the embarrassment of having Conor help me rescue her. I began to feel grateful.

"She must have gone in through one of the runs higher up and got stuck," he said.

With my cheek pressed against the ground, and my arm at full stretch down the hole, I scrabbled away at the earth and stones surrounding Flicka's nose, and gradually her head slipped through. As I widened the hole round her shoulders I realised that she seemed to be hanging head down in the higher tunnel, with her front legs back. There was no way that she could have freed herself.

Eventually she slipped down into the tunnel, and

staggered out into the light. I expected a greeting, a wagging tail, maybe some expression of relief, but she just stood there, looking glum, and as I picked her up she went cold against me and began to shake.

I turned to thank Conor, who had lifted the spade over his shoulder and was preparing to leave.

"That's all right," he said. "But this part of the wood is private. Best you stick to the common."

I tried to say that I was keeping out of the woods, and explain that it was all the deer's fault, but he was already walking away. I called another "thank you" after him and he raised a hand in acknowledgment, but didn't look round.

Lacking the nerve to go the shorter way home though the wood, I climbed back over the ditch and through the fence onto the common - an exercise made doubly difficult by having to carry Flicka at the same time. When I got her home she just shivered in her bed in front of the Aga, and refused to speak to me, or either of the other dogs for the rest of the day...I think she was embarrassed.

When Gerald came home I tried to tell him the story of Flicka's rescue, but had difficulty in getting him to appreciate the drama of it all...there had been a fall in interest rates, which was concentrating his mind to the exclusion of all lesser considerations.

He did bend down to give her a welcome home stroke, but Huggy saw him coming and hurriedly put himself in Flicka's bed, pushing her to the back and giving Gerald a look which meant 'touch her if you dare'.

"I'm seriously going off that dog," he said as he straightened up. "I'm just going to see what Ernie's done with the hay, and have look at the cows; have we got an umbrella?"

A little while later I was startled to see Nasty gallop past the kitchen window glancing over her shoulder, then she stopped and faced whatever was chasing her and stamped an angry foot, before losing her nerve and taking flight again up the drive.

Gerald opened the door and turned to shake the water off the umbrella before leaving it in the scullery.

"That stupid ewe of yours is out again, I tried to herd her back in but she's gone up the drive. Haven't seen her move that fast since the invasion of the killer bees."

"Were you herding her with the umbrella up, or down?" I asked.

"Oh!" he said.

God knows what Nasty thought was after her. Probably a deranged mushroom.

"Leave her," I said, "she'll come back when she's ready."

He looked at me and frowned slightly.

"I think it's about time you went and had your hair done. It's a bit of a mess."

"So would yours be if you'd spent half the day with your head down a rabbit hole," I snapped, more angry than I should have been, because I already knew I looked a mess - I didn't need it confirmed. I would have to spend some time on myself, I realised; Gerald wasn't the type to put up with a scruffy wife for long.

CHAPTER THIRTEEN

Conor had left so quickly after Flicka's rescue that I felt I had not thanked him properly for saving her life, but when I tried to phone him the exchange said his number was ex-directory. I thought about writing, but it seemed silly to write a letter to someone who lived within walking distance; so in the end I decided to take him a thank-you bottle of whisky - Irish, of course.

As I paid for the whisky, Jim, at the pub, told me roughly where to find Conor's cottage, deep in the woods: and explained that the easiest way to reach it was to go through the village, and turn up the second track off the main road after the bridge, so this I decided to do. I was tired of meeting Conor when I was at a disadvantage - this way I could go by car, without the dogs, and arrive composed and unflustered.

The springs on the car complained loudly as it bumped along the gloomy unmade track through the trees. This was Land Rover country. The track ended in a wide, grassy, clearing at the back edge of which stood a small stone cottage, almost covered by a waterfall of white wisteria.

The windows, which struggled to let light in through the overwhelming blooms, were small, with diamond leaded panes. This was the dream cottage I had fondly imagined before we had left London.

Behind the cottage the hill rose steeply, and was covered with a mass of purple rhododendrons. There was no garden as such, and the close-clipped grass went right up to the cottage walls.

On the right hand side the ground sloped away to a marshy pond, where a pair of mallards with a small brood of ducklings were gliding about amongst the reeds, and a moorhen was giving a sharp, tail-flirting alarm call at my intrusion into this secret place.

I don't know why I had assumed Conor would be there in the middle of the afternoon, but there was no answer to my knock on the solid little door. A door too low for him to have entered comfortably, I thought, picturing his tall, lean frame.

I peered through the window beside the door, shading my eyes to see into the darkness, and feeling uncomfortably as though I was spying on him - which of course I was.

It was too dark to see much, but I could make out a desk in the corner of the living room on which stood a computer and a fax machine, looking strangely out of place in a 300 year old cottage. A glimmer of sunlight which had managed to struggle into the room revealed something lying beside the keyboard in front of the computer, and as I focused my eyes into the dim room, I made out the shape of a hand gun. Why did he need a gun like that? Was he really something to do with the IRA? Gerald and I had always treated the village gossip as a joke. What if he caught me peering through the window, and knew that I knew?

Backing hurriedly away, I returned to the car and wrote a quick note of thanks to go with the bottle, then placed them both on the wooden bench seat which was built into one side of the little porch, outside the front door.

Reversing the car carefully, so as not to damage the grass, I put my foot down as I reached the track, bouncing and crashing my way along it to the road, hoping I wouldn't meet Conor on his way up in the Land Rover.

Once more this man had managed to leave me feeling flustered, and he wasn't even there. I decided there was something mysterious about him which it was probably safer not to know.

I told Gerald about the gun, but instead of understanding my discomfort at its discovery, all he wanted to know was what kind of a gun it was. Now that he was the proud owner of a 4.10, he was developing a strong fellow feeling with other gun owners.

Conor was sitting at a corner table in the Royal Oak when we dropped in there a few nights later. He nodded to me and raised his glass slightly, then turned back to the slight, fair-haired man he was drinking with. They were deep in discussion over some papers on the table in front of them. Surely they weren't planning some dastardly IRA deed in the lounge bar of the Royal Oak.

When I voiced this idea to Gerald, he said I had too fertile an imagination, and when was I going to cash in on it by writing "this book you were talking about in January."

The word processor was still in its box, waiting for the darker evenings, still comfortably in the distant future as the evenings were now a little lighter every day. The grass had really begun to grow, and my job as farmer was becoming less demanding as the Primroses and sheep became self sufficient on the new grass. The callouses on my bale-carrying fingers disappeared, and as the ground dried out I swapped my wellingtons for shoes.

I had taken Gerald's advice and had my hair cut

and restyled, and had even dressed in a skirt for him one weekend. It might have pleased Gerald, but when I went down to look at the sheep they all ran away, even Cheap, and I had to change back into trousers before I could get near them.

With a little more time on my hands, I entered the dogs for a Championship show at Bournemouth where Sue, a dog showing friend, thought Huggy might arouse some interest in the dachshund world.

"There aren't many good dogs with that coat colour around," she said. "People are bound to want to use him for stud."

I couldn't deny Huggy this opportunity.

The trip to Bournemouth took up a whole day, and proved to be a mistake, as the show was on a Saturday and it meant leaving Gerald at home, and unsupervised, for the day. At least, I'd thought he was at home.

The dogs behaved well. Huggy won his class, and was presented with a red card, and large frilly red rosette. I hoped this might raise him in Gerald's estimation. Ever since we had had all those 'macho' police dogs on the farm, Gerald had been calling the dachshunds 'long wheelbase rats' and asking why we couldn't have a proper dog.

As Sue had predicted, two people had shown an interest in using Huggy's services at some future date, and I arrived home happy and relaxed.

Before going indoors I wandered round the peaceful farm with the dogs, just to re-assure myself that no disasters had occurred in my absence.

Leaning on the fence of the sheep paddock I was idly scratching Cheap's forehead and automatically counting the flock when, with a start, I realised we had too many sheep. There were four more Oxford Down ewes in the field, fully grown ones.

They were extremely jittery, and I discovered why when I found Gerald, who was leaning on the gate to the Primroses field, admiring the red mounds of gleaming cowhide, slumped on the bright green grass, belching as they regurgitated their cud and chewed it with every sign of contentment.

"Gerald...you promised... no more animals."

"Did you have a good day?" he asked.

"There are four more sheep in the paddock. Where did they come from?"

He put a soothing arm round my shoulders as he walked me back up to the sheep, explaining that he had fetched them from Oxford himself, and saved huge amounts on haulier's fees.

"What in?" was my next question - I couldn't see Gerald using his car to transport sheep.

It turned out that he had borrowed a small open-top trailer from Ernie, which he had roofed over with some chicken wire to make a cage. He must have driven like a maniac to have got to Oxford, done the deal, loaded the sheep and got home before me. No wonder they looked scared.

We stopped at the gate of the sheep paddock for him to introduce his new purchases; one of whom, as I studied them more closely, looked distinctly old. Her face was more grey than black, and her ears drooped sideways.

"That is the ugliest sheep I have ever seen. However old is she?" I asked

"I bought her for her pedigree. She's from a very famous line in this top winning flock in Oxford," he said defensively.

"Has she got any teeth?" I asked, looking at the

scraggy, grey-whiskered beast as it lay there exhausted... too tired after the journey to close its mouth and stop dribbling.

"Of course it has." Gerald didn't sound too sure and I realised that he had forgotten to look. I had read in his sheep book that you have to make sure sheep have a full set of teeth.

"I hope that's the extent of your sheep buying now," I said huffily. "I'm not looking after any more - half that new lot look as if they are going to need round-the-clock nursing any minute. I did a quick sum. "Gerald, do you realise that we now have fourteen sheep and four cows; next year we could find ourselves with eight cows, and - if they all have twins – thirty-three sheep?" I instantly wished I hadn't done this little mathematical exercise. "What else are you planning to surprise me with? It's all very well getting millions of animals in the spring, but when winter comes, looking after that lot is going to be hard work."

"Hardly millions, darling. You always look on the black side. You've got Ernie now to give you a hand on Wednesdays, and you know I'll help. Once we really get a proper system running it will be easy."

He promised that he wouldn't buy any more animals without consulting me, and began to paint a rosy picture of how pedigree Oxford Down and South Devon breeders would be flocking to our door for stock, as Warren Hanger bred animals began to win prizes at the Agricultural Shows.

"Huggy won a prize," I said, fishing the scarlet rosette out of my pocket. Gerald was impressed.

"Well done, little fellow," he said, bending down to stroke Huggy, who ducked out of the way, wondering what he had done to deserve a smack this time.

We had just sat down to our supper when the telephone rang. The voice at the other end was cultured, and its owner sounded rather elderly.

"I understand you have a wirehaired dachshund stud dog."

Huggy looked up from his bed as he felt my eyes on him. I gave him the thumbs up sign.

"That's right; he's black and tan."

"I wonder if we could use him on Nutkin, our bitch?"

I accepted on Huggy's behalf, and asked when her bitch was likely to come in season: only to be told that she was already in season, and it would be convenient for them to come on Monday morning to have her mated?

I knew that the actual day for a successful mating during a bitch's season was crucial, and asked the lady how many days her bitch had been in season. She was a little vague about when Nutkin had started, but Monday would fit in well with their plans as they had a free morning. In the afternoon, of course, they were playing Bridge, and the following day they were off to spend a few days with their daughter and grandchildren in Shropshire.

On Monday I had arranged a dental appointment, but found myself offering to cancel this, as it did not fit in with their plans.

"We will come at eleven o'clock," the lady said.

I suggested that it might be better if they came a little earlier if they had an afternoon appointment; I wasn't sure how long this would all take. Sue had told me tales of dogs who had tied for up to an hour on mating, and once tied it was physically impossible to separate them without injuring them.

But the lady said that it would be very inconvenient to have to come earlier. Her husband did not like to be rushed in the mornings. She also said that darling Nutkin was the sweetest thing, and had never been any trouble and loved everybody. I hoped she would love Huggy.

"Another of your 'loony' dog people?" asked Gerald disparagingly. Huggy's attitude to Gerald had put him off, not only small dogs but the people that went with them.

"It looks as if Huggy has 'pulled' after his win today, and with a bit of luck he'll 'score' on Monday," I told him. Gerald looked across at Huggy with new eyes. Eyes in which £ signs for stud fees were flashing up like a Disney cartoon.

Gerald was a bit pre-occupied on Monday morning; there was an important meeting looming and he'd decided to take an earlier train.

"Check the animals for me, will you?" he called out as he climbed into his car, turned on the radio, and drove away.

I wandered over to where Cheap was standing by the gate.

"I used to get a goodbye kiss," I told him ruefully.

"Baa," he said, lifting his nose to mine, as I bent down to stroke him.

"I think I love you," I said.

"Baa," he agreed.

When I looked at Huggy after his early morning turn in the dog paddock, I found he had rolled in something disgusting, and had at least one flea. I bathed him quickly, blew him dry with the hairdryer, and sprayed him with insecticide. He thought he was going to another show and got very excited, managing to wind

Rudi and Flicka up as well.

At eleven o'clock, on the dot, a gleaming blue Bentley drifted gently to a stop in the farmyard, and Huggy's stud fee went up five pounds.

As I had thought, the couple who got out of this elegant car were elderly, in their early seventies at a rough guess. Nutkin, a little red wirehaired dachshund, hopped out of the car and sniffed around in the farmyard. I bent down and said "Hello" nicely to her, but Nutkin glanced briefly at me, and wrote me off as unimportant. I knew that once you have been written off as unimportant by a dachshund, there is absolutely no point in trying to pursue friendly advances, unless you have a week to spare, a good supply of cooked chunks of liver - and its family are absent.

Abandoning the effort, I led them through to the sitting room, where they sat side by side on the sofa. For appearances' sake I had one more try at establishing some kind of rapport with Nutkin who, sensing my insincerity, would have nothing to do with me.

I fetched Huggy for them to see, in case they wanted to change their minds, as they seemed to be under the impression that Nutkin's babies would look just like her. They gave him a cursory glance and pronounced him suitable. Nutkin's puppies were obviously all going to be red; any black ones would come as a nasty shock. Huggy, being a friendly little chap, looked slightly puzzled at their lack of interest in him, but wagged his tail at Nutkin, who snarled, and climbed on to her lady owner's lap.

"Where are you going to do it?" the lady asked.

"Er, well, I thought I would do it in here. I've got two more dogs shut up in the kitchen," I said.

"Oh dear, well, um, we'll wait in the car," the lady said. Her husband looked panic-stricken. They rose, flustered.

"It may take a little while," I told them; the stories of inordinately lengthy couplings which Sue had told me about still in my mind.

"How long?" asked the lady.

"You had better allow about an hour," I said. "Some dogs have been known to 'tie' for three quarters of an hour."

"Three quarters of an hour?" she gasped; he looked embarrassed, shot Huggy an envious glance, then stared out of the window. "I'd no idea. We had better go to that pub in the village and get some lunch, hadn't we, dear?" she said. "We'll come back for Nutkin at half past twelve."

I couldn't decide which would be worse; having them stay, and die of embarrassment, or attempting a single-handed mating with a potentially uncooperative bitch, who was probably not ready anyway - or maybe she had 'gone off'. She wasn't showing any signs of flirting with Huggy. In fact, her attitude to him was distinctly unfriendly.

Shutting the two dogs in the sitting room, I saw Nutkin's people to the door, where we found Nasty scratching her flank blissfully on the side of the Bentley, and admiring her reflection in its shiny door panel. I chased her out of the way, and apologised for the dull patch of lanolin on the paintwork.

They left, and I went back to the dogs. Nutkin was huddled by the closed door, looking miserable. Picking her up, I sat on the floor with her draped over my leg to stop her collapsing when Huggy mounted.

She didn't collapse, she spun round, and the teeth

meant for Huggy met through the base of my thumb. I yelled and let her go, and she disappeared under an armchair. Huggy crawled in after her, but with a headroom of four inches he couldn't achieve much. He backed out and looked at me. I finished wrapping a handkerchief round my thumb, then lifted the armchair, took hold of Nutkin's collar and dragged her out. She bit me again, and this one *was* meant for me.

I let her go back under the chair, while I went to the kitchen for two pieces of sticking plaster for me, and a crêpe bandage for Nutkin's mouth.

Dragging her out again, I attempted to bandage her mouth shut, whilst fending Huggy off with my feet. It seemed that bitches who played 'hard to get' were a 'turn-on' for him. Nutkin's mouth firmly tied up, we tried again. Huggy mounted, but as soon as she felt him getting somewhere near the right place, Nutkin struggled like a maniac and shook him off.

This went on for half an hour or more, at the end of which time Huggy was an exhausted, panting wreck and I was beginning to lose my temper. The time was galloping towards half past twelve. One more try, I said to Huggy, then we'll give up.

He staggered to his feet and mounted Nutkin, unenthusiastically, and somehow she managed to drag the bandage off her nose with her front paws. She spun round and sank her fangs into Huggy's nose - he screamed and ran, and she dived under the sofa, but Huggy had already taken refuge there and was bleeding profusely all over the carpet.

She shot out, and as I tried to grab her, she jumped on to the sofa; then on to the back, where she ran along it, and took a flying leap on to the sideboard. Sliding right to the end on the polished surface, she knocked off, and smashed, a whisky decanter and a bottle of sherry, before falling off the end onto a chair and, seeming unhurt, retired under the armchair again.

The telephone rang.

"It's me," said Gerald. "I forgot to ask you to take my grey suit to the cleaners today."

"Suit?" I said, stretching the telephone cord to its limit, as I tried to pick up pieces of glass.

"My grey suit...are you listening?"

"Um, yes." I knelt down and peered under the chair trying, to see if Nutkin had been hurt in her fall off the sideboard.

"You're not listening. What are you doing?"

"I'm crawling about in a sea of broken glass and blood."

"What, Hazel? Oh yes...I'm just coming. I've got to go now, Jill. Don't forget the suit. 'Bye."

I replaced the receiver, wondering if Gerald ever really listened to anything I said. Nutkin seemed to be all right, so I collected Huggy and took him to bleed in the kitchen. A quick dab of antiseptic witch hazel on his nose compounded his misery.

It was twenty past twelve. I got a dustpan and brush, a bucket of water and a cloth, and returned to the sitting room. Nutkin had left her hiding place for long enough to register her strongest protest at the events, by depositing a steaming noxious pile in the middle of the room.

I went back into the kitchen for paper towels, and began to repair the damage as best I could before Nutkin's doting owners returned from their nice civilised pub lunch.

I cleared up the broken glass and washed the carpet, but the room still stank of booze, and worse. Pulling a rug over the wet carpet, I opened all the windows, then looked under the chair and called Nutkin ... nicely. I could see the whites of her eyes and the whites of her teeth.

"Bloody stay there then," I snarled back.

What the hell was I going to tell them? I had seriously gone off the idea of dog breeding. Nutkin's owners seemed to think this sort of thing all happened like clockwork, and they were convinced their Nutkin was the sweetest thing. My hand was throbbing and I wondered what time the doctor's surgery opened; it looked like a case for penicillin to me.

I decided on a half-truth for them. Huggy had actually been there, on the first mounting, for about half a second before Nutkin had realised quite what was happening.

They arrived at exactly twelve thirty, all smiles. Nutkin came out of hiding and gave them an ecstatic welcome. They didn't even ask how things had gone, things did not go wrong in their tidy, well-ordered life.

"How much do I owe you?" he asked, taking out his cheque book. I thought that probably about five hundred pounds would cover the damage to the house, and the purchase of a new stud dog to replace the demoralised Huggy.

But found myself saying: "Oh, I didn't get a very good mating. Let's leave it and see if she has any puppies; you can pay me then."

"Oh no," he said. "I insist."

"They didn't tie," I said feebly, thinking this was the understatement of the year. He obviously didn't want to discuss the more sordid side of the business, so I took the proffered cheque and saw them to their car.

The Bentley rolled smoothly up the drive and, as

they rattled over the cattle grid, Nutkin leapt on to the parcel shelf and hurled abuse at me through the rear window. I returned to my wrecked house and injured Huggy, knowing that Nutkin had won. The cancelled session with the dentist would have been infinitely preferable to the morning I had just spent.

I collected Gerald's suit and set off for town, knowing that I was going to weaken and spend some of Huggy's hard-earned money on scones, clotted cream and strawberry jam. It had been a stressful morning.

Gerald walked into the sitting room that evening, sniffed suspiciously and said: "Has your sister been over again?"

I tried to describe my morning to him, but when I reached the part where the whisky decanter got smashed, he suddenly wasn't finding it so funny. Apparently it was a family heirloom which his grandfather had given him, and irreplaceable. He glared at Huggy as if it was his fault, but Hug was too tired to notice.

I decided that I definitely wasn't going to take up dog breeding. None of the books had mentioned the amount of stress that went with it.

Gerald managed to keep his promise not to get any more animals, without first discussing it with me, for just over a week.

CHAPTER FOURTEEN

When I heard Gerald's car come down the drive one evening, and he didn't come straight in, I thought he had just gone down to look at his beloved cows. Then, as I glanced out of the window, I saw him coming out of the stable across the yard.

Shutting the bottom door he leaned on it for a moment, looking inside, then closed the top door as well. This looked suspiciously as if there was something alive in there which was capable of climbing over the bottom door. My heart sank.

He looked slightly guilty as he came in through the back door, and gave me a kiss. As he had tended to forget kisses of late, until reminded, this unsolicited one increased my suspicion.

"What have you bought?" I asked.

"Nothing - what do you mean?"

"You look funny." I rescued a pan of broccoli which was coming to the boil.

"I was just thinking it would be nice to have our own new laid eggs," he said.

"Chickens!...We haven't got a safe pen for chickens. Where are you going to put them?"

My mind skimmed round the farm, but I was right, there wasn't anywhere we could keep chickens safe from the foxes who regularly trotted across our fields at dusk.

"It's not chickens, it's only one."

"Nobody has 'only one' chicken. Where did you get a chicken in London?"

"I'll get some more. It's in the stable. Come and see."

I picked up the mug of coffee I had just started to drink, and took it with me to the stable. Gerald opened the top door and we peered in. I couldn't see anything in the gloom.

"It didn't cost anything," he said. "Hazel's brother wanted a good home for it. He's moving into a flat."

Something stirred at the back of the stable. My eyes began to adjust their focus to the dim light underneath the old wooden manger; then the chicken walked across into the pool of light from the open door, and I began to giggle... and then found I couldn't stop. I think I was relieving some of the pent-up hysteria engendered by our increasingly ham-fisted attempts at animal husbandry. I held on to the stable door, gasping and hiccuping, while the chicken looked at me with its head on one side; spectacular green and black feathers gleaming, and scarlet comb wobbling as it moved.

"It's not that funny," said Gerald in an aggrieved tone.

"It's a cockerel!" I snorted. "A little bantam cockerel. How many new laid eggs were you reckoning to get out of that?"

My ribs hurt as I dissolved again into helpless giggles.

"Watch it!" said Gerald as I spilled hot coffee down his leg. "I know it is a cockerel, but it's a start. I'll get it some hens. He's called Napoleon, by the way."

I coughed and began to get the hysteria under control, as the implications of his last remark struck home.

"Who's going to look after these chickens?" I asked.

"You don't have to look after chickens, they just scratch about in farmyards and the farmer's wife throws them corn occasionally."

"You've been reading too many Janet and John books," I sighed. "They will need a run and a hen house to protect them from foxes. I don't think it's worth the expense."

Gerald pointed out that there was lots of wire and timber lying around the farm; he was sure he could house Napoleon adequately at the weekend, when he had a bit of time. In fact, he thought that if he was going to that much trouble over it, he might as well build up a decent flock, then we could sell eggs at the farm gate and recoup our costs.

"I think I've got a book on chickens somewhere," he said.

"Just a minute," I said, turning away from the stable door to reason with him, but he was already half way back to the house muttering about Rhode Island Reds.

His initial enthusiasm for chicken run building seemed to wane over the next week, and Napoleon became so lonely in the stable, waiting for his hens, that he fell in love with a cabbage I had thrown in for him. Nobody was allowed near his cabbage, and when he wasn't guarding it, he was raping it.

"That bird is getting dreadfully confused. You're going to have to make a pen for him and get him some hens," I said as we stood watching Napoleon, who was daring us to go near his cabbage.

"I'm a bit busy at the moment. I'll give that carpenter chap, Steve, a ring, and see if he can build something."

As we were leaving the stable he took a teasing step

towards the little cockerel, and laughed when all the feathers stood up round Napoleon's neck as he swelled with rage.

"Don't be unkind. How would you like somebody menacing your cabbage?" I said, and pointed out that these chickens were going to be very expensive by the time he had paid Steve's wages for building a run. It would be cheaper to buy eggs.

"All right," he said grumpily. "I'll do it next weekend. Have a look round the farm and see if you can find some suitable wooden posts, and I think there is a roll of wire down in the bottom yard."

On Saturday morning Gerald finally flung some posts and wire together, in the field behind the house.

"Voila! A chicken run," he said.

It looked rather rickety, but it would not have been very kind to say so...I could see he was proud of it, and anyway it's 'ricketyness' was in keeping with most of the other buildings on the farm that hadn't actually fallen down; like the pigsties in the bottom yard. I was quite happy with their picturesque and tumble-down state, because repairing them would entail far too much work, and money, before they could be considered suitable for Tamworths and Gloucester Old Spots and whatever else was currently considered rare in the pedigree pig world.

After lunch we drove over the Downs to a poultry farm, and bought six Rhode Island Red pullets. They were already larger than Napoleon, and I hoped he liked big girls. The poultry breeder then persuaded Gerald to spend a fortune on a sort of chicken Hilton, for Napoleon and his wives to live in. Now this *was* going to look out of place at Warren Hanger.

"I've got a lorry going out your way in about half

an hour," the man said. "If you're going straight home, you can have this lot delivered by about half past four."

The hen house, and pullets, arrived about twenty minutes after we got home, and the two deliverymen erected the sectional hen house with impressive efficiency.

We released the hens from their carrying cage into the pen, and I went to fetch Napoleon. He refused to leave his cabbage, or to let me catch him, until I fetched one of the dogs show cages, and placed the cabbage in the back of it. After frantically dancing round the cage, pecking at the cabbage through the bars, he found the entrance and I shut the door on him.

When we put him in the pen with the hens, he didn't seem to know what they were and crouched by his beloved cabbage, which I had tipped out with him, glaring at the hens with his beady eyes and daring them to approach it. After watching them for quarter of an hour as they wandered about scratching for grubs and ignoring him, he gradually came to his senses and joined them. Five minutes later I removed the yellowing, tattered cabbage, and he didn't notice it had gone. Short memories - chickens, I thought.

Gerald went back to the house, and I wandered down the track to check that Nasty was still in her proper field, and have a quick cuddle with Cheap and tell him about the chickens.

When I got back indoors, Gerald was reading his book on poultry keeping and calculating the profit we would make from the eggs.

"You'll never cover the cost of that chicken house," I said.

Business did not work like that, it seemed, and my mind wandered as I made a pot of tea, and he told me all about the importance of fixed assets.

Half an hour later I opened the door to the garden to let the dogs in; this was their other secure area, and I thought Gerald had let them out when he came in - but they didn't come when I called.

"Gerald - did you let the dogs into the garden?"

"No - they went out of the back door when I came in. I thought they were with you."

"You're hopeless," I fumed, "they'll be miles away down rabbit holes by now, and I haven't a clue where to start digging if they don't come back. I don't want another embarrassing session with that 'gun-toting' Irishman."

"Well I didn't know, did I?"

This was no time for an argument. I collected the leads and set off to hunt for them - but they weren't far away. Gerald had provided their day's sport much nearer to home than usual.

The carnage which greeted me at the chicken run turned my stomach. There were brown feathers all over the run, and the dogs were wandering about, panting and excited. They had killed all six pullets. I found Napoleon's body behind the hen house, and could feel tears trickling down my face as I raged at the dogs, which was rather pointless, as nobody had told them they weren't supposed to kill chickens. They had never seen chickens before.

Their entry point into the run was easily found. Gerald had used an old wire-covered gate that he had found at the back of the barn as the gate for the chicken run, and the wire mesh had rusted and rotted. A butterfly leaning against it would have made a hole, let alone a dachshund crazed with blood lust.

I braced myself to tell Gerald, and dragged the dogs

back to the house on their leads, in a manner of which the RSPCA would not have approved.

He looked up from chapter three of 'Poultry Keeping'.

"Oh, you found them, good. I knew they wouldn't have gone far."

"They didn't. They got no further than the chicken run."

"Don't you let them bother the hens. I don't want them put off laying."

"Their egg-laying days are done, Gerald." I swallowed and blew my nose as the memory of poor little Napoleon's body threatened more tears. "I can't think of an easy way to break this to you...I'm terribly sorry."

"Why are you crying?"

"It's the dogs...the chickens...they've killed them...all of them...even little Napoleon."

Gerald stiffened and turned pale. "You are joking, aren't you? The dogs have only been gone a minute, and they couldn't have got into the run. You are joking, aren't you?"

"The dogs have been gone about half an hour, and I'm sorry but I'm not joking. The chickens are dead. The gate was rotten."

Gerald gritted his teeth and stood up.

"Right! Those dogs have got to go! They're nothing but a headache. I'm not having all the stock on the farm murdered... and they annoy the neighbours."

This was too much.

"You taught them to annoy the neighbours. You encouraged them to bark at every opportunity. I can hardly use my purpose-built dog paddock when any of the Barrington-Smythes are in residence. Every time anyone moves the other side of the fence these three murdering little bastards have hysterics, and I have to get them in."

"They need a good beating; that'll teach them to kill chickens. I'll do it if you won't," he said, picking up a shoe as the handiest weapon with which to bludgeon the dogs into submission.

"You won't! And put that shoe down. It was your fault for not making the run properly, and then letting the dogs out. Anyway, chickens was a stupid idea. It's much cheaper to buy eggs."

We were having our first real row and I began to feel shaky.

"I'm bloody annoyed. I liked Napoleon. What am I going to tell Hazel?" he said.

"I don't know." I didn't care. "You'll have to clear up the bodies, I don't want to do that."

Gerald snatched the tractor keys from the hook by the back door.

"What do you want the tractor for?"

"I'll use the bucket on it to dig a hole to bury them."

"Wouldn't a spade do?"

"It's easier with the tractor," he said as he went out, aiming a vicious kick at Huggy on the way - which he managed to dodge.

The first piece of ground which Gerald chose for the interment of the chickens was just inside the field gate and proved too hard for the tractor bucket to break into, so he drove further across the field towards the stream where the ground was softer - with the result that he got the tractor stuck in the mud.

After a lot of engine revving and wheel spinning, which dug it in even deeper, he got off, leaving it tilted at a crazy angle, and stormed indoors to the phone, where he organised Ernie Challen and his wood-cutter friend to come over on Monday to tow it out.

Then, using a spade, he then dug a rather shallow mass grave for the chickens, swearing, and cursing the dogs every time he put his foot on the spade. The rest of the weekend was spent in an uncomfortable truce. Neither of us mentioned chickens or tractors, and the dogs crept about being very subdued, not knowing quite how to handle both of us hating them.

"What was he doing with it over here anyway?" Ernie asked on Monday morning, when he and Sid arrived on Sid's new tractor.

"Burying chickens," I said.

"I see," said Ernie, who patently did not.

When I went into the shop the following Saturday, Margaret said, " I hear you've lost some hens...fox, was it?"

"Er, yes," I lied. I was beginning to get a bit paranoid; feeling sure that the surrounding farmers were finding the exploits of the new occupants of Warren Hanger Farm more amusing than the average sit-com.

"They're devils when they gets amongst hens, kills the lot, they do. Did they get all yours?"

"Yes...can I have half a pound of that ham - is that one that you cooked yourself?" I had managed to deflect her. Margaret's home cooked hams were superb - she also baked a 'mean' coffee and walnut sponge. By the time I had admired and bought both, she had forgotten the hens.

I hadn't forgotten the horror of finding them, but was beginning to push it to the back of my mind, when Gerald announced that he was going to get some more hens, and a 'proper' cockerel. My heart sank. This was going to involve me in constant vigilance with the dogs, and the opening and closing of house doors.

"I don't think it's a very good idea, Gerald; and what about the run?"

"What do you think I've been doing all morning?" he asked.

I hadn't really thought about it, beyond checking that the tractor was still safely parked in the yard. I had walked the dogs, tidied the house and prepared a salad to go with the ham for lunch. I now noticed that he had a box of nails in one hand and a hammer in the other.

"Can I just have a look at the run before you re-stock it? I know what the dogs are capable of in the way of getting through fences," I said.

"You've no faith in anything I do, have you?" he grumbled.

We went down to the chicken run where, in view of Gerald's hurt remark, I found myself lost for words. I wanted to laugh, but that wouldn't have been a good idea - or kind.

Gerald had boarded in the whole of the six-foot high gate, the one which the dogs had broken through, with half inch thick oak planks. The gate was now so heavy that it was pulling the posts and wire slowly out of alignment as I watched.

"Right – let's see the little buggers get through that," he said triumphantly, tapping the gate with the hammer.

"They won't need to." I pointed. "It's pulled the wire up six inches from the ground round at the back. Don't you think the gate is a mite heavy?"

"Oh! Sod it! Well, I haven't got any more time to spend on it now. Get Ernie to have a look at it on Wednesday."

"What do you mean by 'have a look at it'?" I asked.

"Well, straighten it all up and make it safe - if it wasn't for your damn dogs we wouldn't have this problem."

"And the foxes," I said, thinking of Margaret.

"They're no problem; the hens will be locked in at night."

Ernie duly 'had a look at' the chicken run and made it a new wire gate, muttering that Gerald hadn't said anything about carpentry when he took him on. I took Gerald's stout oak gate and put it ready to use as a wheelbarrow ramp, for pushing muck onto the dung heap, in case I ever had to muck out another cow shed.

Once the run was secure, Gerald went back to the poultry farm and bought a dozen plump, Rhode Island Red hens - already laying wonderful brown eggs, the man assured him - and the handsomest, meanest, most vicious cockerel in the world.

The bird was lethal, he just lived for a good 'punch-up'. I refused to go into the run after the first day, when he had shredded the leg of my jeans, and driven his talons quarter of an inch into the flesh underneath. The wounds had bled copiously, and Gerald had had to take me to the doctor's surgery for an anti-tetanus injection.

Slasher, as he became known, was particularly enthusiastic when engaging Gerald in battle, and I rather suspected that he enjoyed the bird's uninhibited violence. He had placed a yard broom beside the gate of the chicken run, which initially he had just used to fend off the demented cockerel, but after Slasher had dodged the broom and raked his talons down Gerald's wrist, he took to bashing him in earnest with the broom head.

Slasher loved it...he spent most of the day waiting for Gerald to come home and try to collect the eggs.

The next time we were driving past the poultry farm where Gerald had bought the birds, I asked him to stop, which he did with rather bad grace, and I went in to complain to the poultry breeder about Slasher's temperament. Gerald waited in the car.

The poultry farmer apologised, but assured me the problem was not unusual and was easily remedied. He gave me detailed instructions as to how to subdue Slasher.

All the way home in the car I was psyching myself up to the level of confidence needed to enter the chicken run, and put his advice into practice. Gerald, now very amused, was threatening to film my performance.

Pulling on two pairs of jeans, and some leather gardening gloves, I went down to the run. Gerald was already there, poking the broom handle through the wire at the enraged cockerel.

Between us we cornered Slasher, who was momentarily thrown off balance by having two adversaries to cope with. Gerald pinned him down with the broom, while I picked him up and tucked him under my arm, as the poultry breeder had instructed. I then proceeded to stroke Slasher, gently, all round his neck and head, cooing sweet nothings and words of love to him, as I carried him slowly round the run for ten minutes.

The cockerel was totally embarrassed. Nobody had ever done anything quite so demeaningly awful to him before; he didn't know how to handle it. All his hens were watching - he could have died. His eyes glazed over with stress and shame. I finished cuddling him, and with a final stroke along his lethal beak and the side of his face, I placed him very gently on the ground, where he sat hypnotised and unmoving for five minutes, before ruffling up his feathers, shaking himself and walking slowly away.

I'm sure there was disappointment on Gerald's face, until he went into the run later and was attacked with all the usual ferocity.

"Your cure didn't work; he went for me like he always does," he told me, as he came in breathless from trying to collect the eggs.

"The man said it was foolproof." Picking up the leather gloves, I went back to the run with him to see what had gone wrong.

"You stay here," I told him bravely.

Gerald handed me the broom.

"No – I'll try it without." I was going to need a medal for this. Wasn't there one for 'Extreme Valour in the face of the Enemy'?

Slasher watched me as I opened the gate, and checked me over for weapons.

"Hello, my lovely boy," I crooned.

He gave me one horrified look, and scuttled round behind the hens. Problem solved. Each individual wishing to enter Slasher's domain had to make peace with him first. I told Gerald he would have to go in and cuddle Slasher as well, and handed him the gloves.

"I'm buggered if I'm going to start cuddling chickens," said Gerald.

It was as I had suspected. Gerald looked forward to his vicious encounters with Slasher, and was rather disappointed with the new timid version I had created. He refused to cuddle him, and they resumed their terrible, violent, and sometimes bloody battles which both thoroughly enjoyed, but at the first sight of me, Slasher would make himself scarce in amongst the hens and pretend I wasn't there.

The hens did lay remarkably fine brown eggs, but by the time Gerald had kept Hazel, and various other colleagues at work, supplied, and I had given Ernie a regular half dozen a week to keep him sweet, there were none left to sell, and I sometimes had to buy some for us from the shop - and it would definitely have been cheaper to buy eggs, than food for the chickens.

With farming there never seemed to be time to stop and relax. Once the Warren Hanger flock of chickens was established, we found that we needed to concentrate on the sheep again.

CHAPTER FIFTEEN

As the weather became warmer, the sheep, still clothed in their winter wool, had begun to pant and loll about in the shade of a large oak tree, near the centre of their field. One of the nice things about the farm was that all of the fields had some shelter for the animals, either from hedges, or free-standing mature trees like the oak.

Gerald began to study the advertisements for sheep shearing equipment in Farmers Weekly.

When Erica dropped in for coffee one morning, she noticed one of these advertisements for electric clippers which Gerald had marked in the magazine, and fell about laughing at the thought of him shearing his own sheep, but did have the grace to say that even she wouldn't take on that job.

"Leave it to the professionals," she said, and promised to arrange for a firm of travelling shearers to visit us, and then gave me a list of things which we would have to do before the shearers arrived.

At the top of this list was: 'get a wool sack'...would the Chancellor mind sitting on something else for a couple of days, I wondered.

Then we had to register with the Wool Marketing Board, to sell the fleeces. If you have more than five sheep you are obliged to sell the wool to the Wool Marketing Board. Beyond relieving the sheep of their heat problem, neither of us had considered what we would do with the wool.

Erica said it was important that the sheep be

brought in under cover the day before shearing. Apparently wet wool and electric clippers are not a good combination.

Actually, if your name was Cheap, the most important piece of information was that I should tell the shearers he was a wether, because all the wethers have usually been eaten by the time they're his age.

"If the shearers don't see the usual ram equipment when they tip him up," Erica said, "they'll assume he's a ewe, and are liable to shear off the remaining essential piece of his anatomy with that first strip down the tummy."

The night before the shearers were due to arrive, we brought the sheep in onto a clean dry concrete floor in the barn, so that they would be in pristine condition the next day.

They pee-ed, poo-ed and rolled about in it all night, with the result that by morning they looked, and smelt, revolting.

As it was a weekday, and Gerald was in London, Erica had lent me Terry, one of their farm hands, to help with the operation. We were all ready to go when, just before the shearers were due to arrive, a battered blue van pulled into the yard, and a very attractive lass with long curly brown hair got out. A black and white collie dog peered out of the muddy rear windows of the vehicle.

"Hello, can I help you?" I said.

"You can carry these over to the pen," she said, handing me a pair of electric clippers. Terry began helping her to unload a rubber mat from the back of the van. The collie jumped out and eyed the sheep, which huddled nervously together. The girl snapped her fingers, and the dog jumped back into the van and lay down.

I pulled myself together with difficulty. The only shearing I had ever seen done had been on television, by Fosters-swilling Australian male chauvinists. Terry, grinning with delight, had already established that this vision's name was Sonia (not even Sheila!). What with Sam, the artificial inseminator, and now Sonia, girl-power seemed to be alive and well in the countryside.

Together, she and Terry set up the stands which carried the clipper leads from the power point in the barn, plugged the leads in, and tested the clippers - the older ewes twitched their ears and flinched at the sound. I asked if there was anything I could do, and was detailed off to push the sheep through the gate to Sonia, one at a time.

As this seemed to be one of the dirtier jobs, in view of the flock's nocturnal activities, I asked Terry what he was proposing to do. It seemed that he would stay close to Sonia, ready to roll the fleeces up, when she had removed them. When I suggested we should swap duties, he said there was an art to fleece rolling, which apparently took years to learn, and if they were badly presented the Wool Marketing Board wouldn't accept them.

I gave up, grabbed a passing ewe and held it as it struggled, pressing it against the gate with both hands and a knee. It was very strong. Sonia nodded and opened the gate and I forced it, fighting every inch of the way, through to her. She picked it up with two fingers, flipped it over onto its bottom, and in a blurred, clipper-buzzing minute or two it was naked.

Deeply impressed, I pushed another one through the gap, and admired her mastery over the sheep, and the neat way the clippers striped their way through the fleece, which was a lovely clean pale yellow underneath the filth.

The third sheep through the gate was Cheap, who was much larger and fatter than the ewes. Sonia pushed her curly hair out of her eyes with the back of her hand, and bent over Cheap, but she slipped as she pulled him over to park him on his bottom, and they both collapsed on the rubber mat.

Cheap got up and started to walk away. Quickly latching the gate, I chased after him, grabbed him and dragged him back to where Terry was gallantly helping Sonia to her feet - I wasn't sure whether he needed to put his arm round her to do this, but she didn't seem to mind. I handed Cheap back to her. "Oh-baa!" he said pitifully.

"Serves you right for trying to eat the whole fucking field yourself," she told him, swinging him over and beginning to run the clippers down his plump belly.

As I was giggling at this wonderfully appropriate piece of alliteration, I suddenly remembered... "Stop!" I shrieked. Sonia turned the clippers off and looked enquiringly at me, and I explained that he was not a ewe and please would she be careful. She grinned and nodded towards her left hand.

"It's all right, I've got my finger on it," she said.

Nasty, by dint of barging her way round the pen, had managed to avoid being caught, but now she was the only one left. As I advanced, she backed into a corner, glared at me and stamped a front foot threateningly. Then, just as I lunged for her, she barged past me, bounded over a three-foot hurdle and disappeared behind the barn. I hadn't realised sheep could jump that high. This was probably how she had been escaping from her field.

Leaving Sonia and Terry to shear Henry, who had been penned separately, I went after Nasty, but she had vanished. After a fruitless search, I decided I couldn't hold Sonia up any longer, and went back to settle up with her for the morning's work. She suggested that as there were only a few sheep, she could take the wool sack of fleeces in payment. They were worth only a little more than paying her to do the job, and it saved me the hassle of finding out how to get them to the Wool Marketing Board.

Terry and Sonia exchanged telephone numbers, and she packed up her equipment in the van, and left.

I found Nasty later, trapped in the old pig sties. In pushing her way in, she had dislodged a piece of low corrugated roofing, which had slipped down behind her, shutting her in.

With Nasty confined in this small space, now seemed as good a time as any to further my shepherding skills. I couldn't call Sonia back to shear just one sheep. I fetched scissors and Cheap's halter.

After ten minutes of unbelievable violence and foul language, I had the halter on her, I also had a badly bruised shoulder and a crushed foot. I was trying to pull her into a corner where I could secure the halter rope to a handy rail, when she fell down.

Grabbing a piece of orange baler twine which was lying on the floor beside me, I quickly tied her front feet together then, kneeling beside her, spent half an hour hacking off most of the wool on one side. Then, pulling her to her feet, still hobbled, I spent another hour and a half snipping away at the greasy, lanolin-soaked fleece on the other side, reaching as far underneath as I could while she struggled.

When I tried to straighten up, I couldn't. My back was red-hot agony. I untied the baler twine and released her front legs, while she glared at me with evil, slanting eyes. She looked awful; pink and bare in some places, with straggly tufts sticking up in others, and an untidy fringe underneath. She looked as if she had been savaged by giant moths.

There was no way Nasty's fleece was going to be rolled up neatly; it was spread in snippets all over the floor. Wool Marketing Board rules or not, I swept it all into a wheelbarrow, took it out to an empty field and had a bonfire.

"What on earth's happened to Nasty?" were Gerald's first words as he came in that evening.

"I sheared her," I said. There was no one else I could blame. I was just glad it was Nasty, not one of his sheep.

"My God! Whatever with...your teeth?"

"No, your razor." This sent Gerald into the bathroom at speed to check on his new electric razor. I heard it buzz a couple of times as he tried it.

"Very funny! Why didn't the shearers do her with the others?"

I explained about Sonia and Nasty and Terry, and Gerald said he was beginning to envy me. I was having all the fun while he was slaving away in town.

I wasn't sure whether I was; my back certainly wasn't. There was a huge black bruise on my foot, which my slipper was rubbing against, and my grazed shoulder was very sore. But there had been a couple of laughs during the day, and the sheep were now cool and comfortable; they had gone cavorting back to their field, springing into the air with the new lightness of having cast off their winter woollies.

There was one physical benefit which had arisen from my attempt at sheep shearing - my hands were particularly soft and beautiful after the hours spent covered in the lanolin from Nasty's wool. I pushed away the sensuous thought that macho Australian shearers probably held their cans of Fosters with incredibly smooth, strong hands.

Just as we were relaxing after the excitement of the shearing, and beginning to really feel as if we were starting to farm properly, the relentless roll of the seasons pushed us into our next job, which left both of us aching and exhausted.

CHAPTER SIXTEEN

"The animals are not keeping up with all this grass," said Gerald, doing his morning stock-check through binoculars, from the landing window. It was another warm, drizzly day, perfect grass-growing weather.

"Perhaps we should get some more cows," he mused aloud.

This remark jerked me out of my early-morning torpor, as I stumbled towards the bathroom.

"You promised, Gerald, you promised, no more animals, I can't cope with any more... or rather, I won't be able to when they've all had babies."

"We'll have to; this lot are just not keeping up with the grass. The place is turning into a jungle."

"Hay!" I said, remembering that Erica had said they would start haymaking soon. I suddenly realised that we too were farmers, and should also be making our own hay. Somehow I had assumed that it arrived, ready baled, on a lorry.

"Hey what?" said Gerald, putting the binoculars back in their case.

"No, hay...dried grass... we make it. Erica and Donald are about to start haymaking."

"Oh hay, yes, of course...I'll get a...what do I need to make hay with?" he asked, his eyes lighting up at the prospect of shopping for large expensive lumps of farm machinery.

"A contractor," I said. I'd heard Margaret in the shop, talking to John, the son of a neighbouring farmer, about some contract work he was doing. "He'll have his own machinery."

Though disappointed at being deprived of an expensive shopping expedition, Gerald brightened up when he realised I was suggesting the lad with the enormous green and yellow Renault tractor, which often held us up when we were driving along the lane.

I carried on towards the bathroom with a sigh of relief. The thought of this tractor working on his farm obviously appealed to Gerald, and he seemed to have forgotten about buying in new cows.

"Can you ring him and see if he can come in and cut it today?" he called.

"It's raining," I answered, through toothbrush and foam.

"Well, that won't matter for cutting it; it will have dried out by the weekend."

I rinsed my mouth. "I seem to remember something about making hay while the sun shines. Why don't we just hand the job over to John and let him decide when to cut it? He's probably been making hay all his life."

Later I telephoned John who agreed to fit us in with his busy schedule, when the weather was right, and said to leave it to him to decide when he would come.

It continued to rain for several days, allowing Gerald time to send Hazel to Foyles book shop in search of books about haymaking. She also bought him a present of a rather terrifying book about self-sufficiency, where all the smaller livestock seemed to be housed in recycled plastic fertiliser bags. I think she'd been watching too many episodes of 'The Good Life' on television.

With two books on pasture management, Gerald suddenly became an expert on grass, and took me on guided tours of the farm, explaining the nutritional values of Timothy and Italian rye grass, while the dogs showed how beneficial it can be to the coat if one rolls in it.

"Get the dogs off there," he said. "I might want to make silage out of it."

I reminded him that we still had the clamp of silage which we had bought from Ernie Challen, and which he had said would probably last us through next winter.

John arrived one lunchtime after a breezy, sunny morning which had dried the dew off the grass, and left it perfect for cutting. The huge green and yellow tractor, with mowing machine attached, trundled down the drive; and I went out to show him which fields we wanted cut.

John did not look like the stereotypical farmer. He was well over six feet tall and very thin, with the kind of long slim hands which I had once seen described in a palmistry book as 'spiritual'. He had a lean face, a nice warm smile and long brown hair. The nearest thing to Jesus I have ever seen driving a tractor. No flowing robes though; he was sensibly dressed in dungarees and a green and yellow baseball cap, with Renault written on it. Was this the height of sartorial elegance on the farm...matching hat and tractor?

He cut all three fields, and by the time he left in the evening, the farm was beginning to smell heavenly.

Gerald and I strolled around these fields for the next two evenings, taking in deep draughts of the sweetly scented drying hay. The dogs enjoyed running on the short grass between the rows, eating the remains of mice and a grass snake, which had not managed to avoid the mower.

This blissful stage didn't last very long. The

weather held and John came back twice to turn the hay - he called it 'tedding' - then once to row it up into long lines ready for the baler. Then again, late on the Saturday morning, to bale it, as the weather forecast was promising thunder.

We had planned a relaxed lunch at the pub, but we found ourselves scrapping this idea – indeed, any idea of lunch - and began following the baler with its rhythmic chunk, chunk, chunk as it picked up and compressed the hay into tight bales before regurgitating them out on to the field for us to pick up.

Under John's instruction we stacked them in small towers of eight bales at a time, around the field. He had finished baling all three fields before we were halfway through the second one, and he took the baler away, returning half an hour later with a large trailer, onto which we began to load the bales. The trailer was high and the bales got heavier and heavier, and haymaking ceased to be any kind of fun. Those who wax lyrical about it have never done it. Never experienced the headaches, the soreness of hands and arms pricked by sharp hay stalks, and the sweat which attracts the flies, and the sheer exhaustion.

There was no question of taking a break from this nightmare of blazing sunshine, and air unbreathably thick with the promise of thunder. The weather forecast had said there might be rain later in the day.

These conditions had reduced Gerald and me to physical wrecks by mid-afternoon, but, driven by the thought that we could lose all our beautiful hay to the approaching storm, we worked on grimly, not speaking, backs aching, hands raw from the baler twine.

We went past hunger, but not thirst, consuming several bottles of lemonade and two six packs of lager -

which gave me a headache - and towards dusk, when the lager ran out, we even drank water.

John spent most of the time on the top of the trailer, stacking the load properly, but when he did descend to ground level, he tossed the bales up on the top of the stack with a pitchfork as if they were weightless. Each time the trailer was filled, John would drive it to the barn for unloading. Gerald and I would trudge wearily behind, trying to convince ourselves that this brief respite would bring us the strength to continue, as the bales now needed lifting again to be stacked in the barn.

Eventually the final trailer-load was completed, and John backed it in under the barn just as the first few heavy drops of rain spattered out of a navy blue sky, onto the corrugated iron roof. He graciously said we could leave unloading this trailer until the following day as he had to get off to the gym, to do some weight training.

That evening we sat slumped and scarlet-faced in front of the television, too exhausted to talk, hands and arms stinging from hundreds of small scratches from the hay stalks.

Somehow we had managed to spread hay over most of the house by the time we had bathed and changed. Hay was blocking the waste pipe from the bath, and although I shook and brushed all our dirty clothes outside the back door, I eventually had to call out the service engineer to remove about half a bale from the working parts of the washing machine.

By Wednesday, though, the aches and pains had diminished, we had unloaded the last trailer and stood congratulating ourselves on the neatly stacked bales of our first successful hay harvest. Gerald took a photo of it to show Hazel!

Nasty arrived and admired it with us, with the result that I spent the next two days nailing chicken wire round the bottom of the stack to try and preserve it for the winter. Then had to fix another layer higher up, as Nasty demonstrated how closely related sheep were to goats, in their ability to stand on their hind legs to reach the higher bits. I decided it really was time to find out exactly how the ewe was escaping from her present field.

Early next morning, having satisfied myself that she was dozing in the sunshine with the rest of the flock, I sat on the wall at the bottom of the garden and watched her. The sheep dozed, they grazed, they drank and they dozed again. I got cramp. Nasty was usually out by now, demanding cake at the kitchen window.

Eventually she rose to her feet and shook herself like a dog. At that moment I sneezed and gave my position away. She saw me, walked up to the gate and asked to be let out.

"You get out the usual way," I called to her. She waited a little longer, then went back to her sunny patch and lay down again. I gave up.

Ten minutes after I had returned to the house, Nasty appeared at the kitchen window looking expectant...then disgruntled, when I tossed out a couple of bread crusts. Occasionally, in extreme circumstances, like when I hadn't been to the shop, she would settle for crusts, but they were taken up with much mouthing and spitting out again, before she resigned herself to the lack of cake.

Gerald came home that evening with some special homeopathic cream which Hazel had given him for his 'poor hands'. He didn't offer me any. Never mind, I thought, I can always rub my 'poor hands' on a passing sheep to extract some lanolin.

I telephoned Erica to boast about our superb hay crop, but she was less than impressed because they had still had some lying out when the storm broke.

"How much did you cut?" she asked.

"About eight acres," I said proudly.

She laughed. "That's less than the smallest of our fields." In an instant we were back in childhood days of 'my rabbit's had seven babies, yours only had five.'

We were laughing about this, as I described the physical agonies we had suffered carting the bales.

"Hazel even went out and bought some homeopathic hand cream for Gerald," I told her.

"You want to watch out she isn't offering to massage his sore back as well...she isn't, is she?"

"Don't be silly, Hazel lives with a very charming young man; they are very happy. Gerald's invited them down for the day next Sunday."

Hazel and Alan arrived on Sunday morning – well, nearly arrived. I suddenly noticed their car stuck half way up the drive where Nasty was stretched out on her side, sound asleep. Alan got out of the car, walked carefully round Nasty and arrived at the yard gate looking distraught.

"Hi, Jill...there's a dead sheep in your drive!"

Nasty suddenly woke up, and Hazel screamed. Gerald came out of the kitchen.

"I thought I heard somebody scream. Oh! Hello, Alan. Who screamed?"

"Hazel," I said. "Nasty rose from the dead."

Alan was laughing with me, but Gerald was rushing up the drive to save Hazel. Nasty saw him coming and took off across the field.

It wasn't the best of starts. Hazel and Alan were

both smartly dressed in suits, but carrying a small hold-all, and while I made coffee they disappeared upstairs, returning a little while later rather self-consciously dressed in jeans and sparkling white trainers.

We walked them round the farm and introduced Hazel to the Primroses. She knew almost more about them, their state of health and pregnancies, than I did, but she was overawed by their size, and refused Gerald's offer to escort her across the field to meet them properly.

Gerald had booked lunch at the pub, and we had just sat down and were ordering from the blackboard, when Hazel, looking across the room behind me, said: "Who's that? He looks familiar."

I half turned and found myself staring into Conor's blue eyes. I couldn't pretend I hadn't seen him, so smiled and nodded. He nodded back, but didn't smile.

"It's a wild Irishman who lives in the woods. There's talk in the village that he is something to do with the IRA," I told her quietly.

"Don't be silly, Jill. He's just a keeper or something, Hazel. Jill's dogs keep getting into trouble with him. Now what are you all having?"

Later in the afternoon, Gerald took Alan down to the chicken run, where after a running battle with Slasher, they managed to collect half a dozen eggs for them to take back to town.

"You should have come, Hazel," said Alan. "That's not a cockerel they've got there, it's a pterodactyl."

After tea, when they were beginning to look a little glazed after two hours of listening to Gerald's plans for the cows, and studying brochures of the latest thing in cattle crushes, they changed back into their town clothes and set off back to London.

I took the dogs for a wander round the farm. It was a glorious late June evening with a clear sky and an enormous full moon rising. A young owl screeched 'tiu-whit, tiu-whit' in Conor's wood, to be answered by the more mellow quavering 'whoooo' of its parent. I leaned on a field gate, while the dogs wandered about. The peace of the place wrapped itself around me, and I knew that I had fallen in love with this little patch of England. Nothing would get me back to living in 'town' again. I thought for a moment of Alan and Hazel, by now safely back in London, and realised that I had forgotten to ask her where she thought she had seen Conor before.

CHAPTER SEVENTEEN

Gerald opened the letter carrying a Birmingham postmark, and smiled.

"The cattle crush is coming on Tuesday - now we'll be able to hold the cows properly for the vet to do the pregnancy tests. We can use it to weigh them as well."

I was all for having the cattle confined in an iron cage while we dealt with them. I don't think I had been bruise-free since we had arrived at the farm.

"Where do you want them to put it?" I asked.

"Oh, somewhere in the bottom yard. I'll move it with the tractor when I get home."

"Are you sure you wouldn't like them to put it in its final resting place? There doesn't seem to be much point in moving it twice."

Especially when the second move would be made by Gerald, who had still not quite mastered the art of tractor driving, let alone jiggling with the hydraulics, but it was wiser to keep this thought to myself.

"No, I can move it," he said. "They're designed to be moved by a tractor."

I decided to ask them to unload it in the middle of the yard, with plenty of space around it.

On Tuesday, finding I was out of biscuits to offer the crush delivery men when they arrived, I went up to the shop and queued behind a grim-faced lady, who had opened a box of six eggs taken from a small stack on the counter. These eggs were privately supplied by a local farmer's wife. The lady checked each one carefully.

"Are you sure these eggs are free range?" she asked Margaret suspiciously.

"Oh yes," was the reply. "One of 'er 'ens got run over the other day."

The grim lady sniffed and said she would try half a dozen.

The wonderful thing about this exchange was that neither of them found it remotely amusing. I busied myself along a shelf of packets of biscuits, and when I reached the counter was able to put my smile down to Margaret's little grand-daughter, who was busy counting apples in a cardboard box on the floor: one, two, three, four, nine, ten, eleven, eight: which, of course, was the correct answer.

The crush arrived late in the afternoon, just when I was beginning to think it wasn't coming. As usual, I was alone on the farm when the large flatbed lorry pulled up in the yard, carrying just one green metal crush, strapped up against the driver's cab. The driver was also alone, and there didn't appear to be any kind of winch, or lifting gear on the lorry.

"Is the boss about?" asked the driver.

"I'm the boss," I told him.

"Oh," he said.

"How are you going to get that off?" I asked, looking at the huge, extremely heavy lump of ironwork on the lorry.

"Well, I had hoped someone was going to give me a hand. You have got a JCB, haven't you?"

"A what?" I did know what a JCB was, but was startled by the assumption that it was standard farm machinery.

"A JCB," repeated the driver.

"Well – no. We've got a tractor; but I don't drive

it," I added hurriedly.

"Well, I don't want to hang about too long. I've delivered five of these today, this is the last one and I have to get back to Birmingham tonight."

"How did you get the others off?"

"They all had JCBs," he answered.

My God, I thought, they *are* standard farm equipment. I offered up a little prayer that Gerald would never stumble across this fact. The thought of the damage he might do with a JCB was awe-inspiring. Only last week, he had knocked the corner and two roofing sheets off the feed store with the tractor bucket. Nasty, who had been foraging in there at the time, had nearly had a heart attack.

The lorry driver was looking at me. At that moment Terry's van came down the drive, and I remembered that Erica had said she would get him to drop off some foot trimming shears for the sheep. Cheap was lame and she thought it would be good for me to learn sheep chiropody on him, as he was so tame.

Relief flooded through me; help was at hand. I also remembered that there was a JCB working down the road, clearing out a ditch.

Terry took over and the decision was made to lift the crush off the lorry with the tractor forks. He fetched the tractor, and positioned the forks under the crush; but then discovered that the lorry was so high that the forks were already fully extended and could provide no lift.

I got into my car and went off to bribe the JCB driver. Somehow word went round, and Ernie Challen and old George, from the village, turned up to see the fun and offer helpful advice. Then, unable to contain themselves, these two pensioners also climbed laboriously onto the lorry to lend a hand.

The cattle crush must have weighed well over a ton, and kept moving and tipping ominously as willing hands manoeuvred it into position on the edge of the lorry. The sight of all these people courting death was terrifying. I had never liked the word crush when it was applied to cattle, but it had suddenly reverted to its original meaning in my mind. I could see the headline - Old Age Pensioners Crushed to Death in Horrific Farm Accident.

I went indoors to see if I could find the farm insurance policy. I couldn't. Gerald's filing system, without Hazel to make sense of it, consisted of two cardboard boxes untidily stuffed with papers. I put the kettle on and, as it boiled, saw the lorry disappearing up the drive towards Birmingham, without the cattle crush.

I braced myself and went outside to find that the crush was unloaded safely, and Terry was just manoeuvering it under the open end of the barn with the tractor. No one was dead, or even seriously injured, and everyone came in for a celebratory drink and pieces of elastoplast for the odd mangled finger.

Gerald was thrilled with his new toy when he arrived home, and went straight out to play with it. I was so relieved that no one had been hurt, that I went along with his request that I stand inside the crush while he adjusted the weighing mechanism. He couldn't seem to get it right. It was registering about eleven pounds heavier than it ought to be.

After an argument in which he insisted that I was heavier than I said I was - which was especially galling because I had just struggled to lose four pounds - we suddenly realised that Huggy was sitting quietly in the gloom at my feet.

Gerald demonstrated the various uses to which the crush could be put. It had all sorts of winches and pulleys and ropes, and there were some odd-shaped wooden blocks in a bag. It turned out that these were for tying the cows' legs onto, to enable the cutting of their toenails. There was also a sort of canvas sling, for suspending the cows to prevent them from falling on you while you cut their toenails.

As it was too late in the evening to start fetching the Primroses in for weighing, Gerald practised on other things. A bale of hay, two of the dogs, me again, himself, and Nasty who wandered in to investigate and found herself trapped.

At the weekend Gerald and I drove one of the new Primroses into it for a test run. It was found to be a rather tight fit for a fully grown South Devon cow, and it was not long before the more pregnant members of the herd had to be excused from the weekly weighing sessions, after Hippo got jammed in the crush for five frightening minutes. Gerald was just about to send for the vet, when I thought of the can of cooking oil in the kitchen.

We poured and massaged the oil all over her sides until, with a loud 'moo', the exhaling of which probably just slimmed her a fraction, she managed to slide free.

Watching one very sticky cow walk back across the field to her friends, who obligingly began to lick the oil off her, Gerald debated over whether he should try and send the crush back to Birmingham with a complaint that it was too small. But just as my blood pressure was rising at the thought that loading it up was probably more dangerous than unloading, he realised that it would be perfect for weighing the calves when they arrived.

"Do you weigh new-born calves?" I asked, with visions of sending cards announcing the births, to our friends.

'To Primrose and Angus, a son, weighing two hundredweight.'

"We'll need to weigh the half-bred ones for the market, we won't be keeping them; they'll have to go for veal or something."

"Oh, not veal, Gerald! That's cruel. Animal Rights people demonstrate about keeping calves in crates. You can't do that."

"For heavens' sake, Jill, you're going to have to get used to the idea that we're farmers now; there's no room in this game for sentiment."

"I'm not at all sure I want to be a farmer; it always seems to boil down to killing things. Couldn't we get rid of the cows...to good homes, of course... and just keep the sheep for their wool?"

"Don't be daft," he said. "You'll get used to it."

Had Gerald always been this hard, I wondered, or had it taken farming to expose this side of his character? I knew I wouldn't get used to it, as he said; it is not generally in the nature of the female to nurture and rear babies for them to be killed.

What I didn't realise was that my baby nurturing-days were coming round again faster than I thought.

CHAPTER EIGHTEEN

It was halfway through July when I first realised there was something different about Nasty. Gerald had just come up from the bottom yard, where he had been building a calving pen for the first pregnant Primrose.

"Your ewe's down there bothering Henry," he said. "I've tried chasing her off but she won't leave him alone."

I put a halter on Cheap and set off down the steep track to the foot of the hill, and the small field where Henry lived.

Behind this field, and our boundary, was an area of wild and tangled scrub made up of young birch trees and bracken, with ferns and low willows in the marshier parts. This small jungle stretched up along the end of the wood to the common; and an odd sound was coming from it - an almost hypnotic two-tone, 'churring'. It could only be a night-jar...but it was mid morning.

I pulled Cheap to a halt, so that I could listen properly. I had only ever heard them on radio nature programmes before.

"It is a night-jar," I told my woolly friend. He rubbed the side of his face on my knee, which I took for agreement. Somewhere I had seen them called goatsuckers, though the idea of a goat suckling a night-jar seemed more than a little bizarre. Another of their names, fern owl, made more sense if you looked at its habitat; which, we are constantly being told, they are losing to cultivation. Not much fear of them being affected on our small, and increasingly untidy, patch, I thought. Though they could possibly be driven off by the stream of swear words coming from the direction of the bottom yard. I found out later that the cause was a moment's inattention with a hammer, which had resulted in a double injury, first to Gerald's thumb, then to his toes as the pain made him drop the hammer.

Cheap and I hurried on. Gerald was developing an uncomfortable habit of managing to shift the blame for most of his ills onto other people - like me, crossbred sheep, and the dogs.

"Baa," said Nasty as Cheap and I reached her. "I want to marry Henry."

"Baa," said Cheap nervously, which meant: "You're stark, raving mad; that ram's dangerous."

I tied Cheap to a fence post and went into Henry's field to chase him away from the gate, so that Nasty would get lonely and come back with us.

"Hey, don't frighten him," said Gerald, dragging a wooden rail round from behind the shed with his good hand. Actually, Henry wasn't frightened. He and I had been getting on quite well recently. I never visited him without a pocket full of sheep nuts, and having pushed him away from the gate I deposited a handful of nuts on the ground to distract him while I led Nasty away.

We stopped in the bottom yard to admire Gerald's new cow pen, and Nasty nudged at my pocket. "I'm starving," she baa-ed.

"You can't be, you great fat thing," I told her.

Gerald went off round the corner to fetch some more nails, saying something about talking to sheep being one of the first signs of madness, but I hardly heard him because I'd just realised what I had said.

I stared, with a growing feeling of horror, at Nasty...she was fat, but not all over; there were just two large bumps sticking out, one on each side. As I watched, one of the bumps moved with a sort of rolling action under the wool.

"Oh Christ! Henry, you bastard!" I said. That must have happened the day Henry arrived on the farm. At least I knew the date and, hurriedly counting up on my fingers, I worked out that Nasty had about three weeks to go before she lambed... nobody lambs in August! How on earth was I going to tell Erica?

"All right, petal - you can have extra food from now on," I told her.

We met Gerald again as we headed for the feed store.

"I thought you were putting her back in the top paddock. Where are you going?" he asked.

"I'm taking her to see her solicitor," I told him. "You can expect to receive a paternity suit shortly."

"What are you talking about?"

"She's pregnant, from that time you let Henry rape her."

"Pregnant! Good old Henry!" He was amused.

"Lambs are supposed to be born in the spring, Gerald, not the bloody autumn."

"Well, at least it's proved Henry is fertile. That's good. Never mind paternity suits, you ought to be paying me a stud fee."

"The proving stud is usually free," I countered, "and anyway I didn't want Nasty to have babies. I only wanted her for mowing. What am I going to do with them?"

"It's going to be twins, is it? Send them to the butcher, we'll keep one for the freezer. It's good really; it'll give you some practice at lambing before the important ones come."

"Eat Nasty's babies!" I felt sick.

"Well, they'll only be half breeds, won't they? We won't be keeping them." He returned to hammering six-inch nails into the post and rail calving pen.

Cheap, Nasty and I set off slowly back up the hill. What had happened to the charming, gentle man I had married? Farming was turning him into some kind of brutal, unfeeling, agricultural snob.

The night-jar still 'churred' away in the distance, but now the sound failed to lift the depression that was settling over me. I was beginning to lose control over this new venture of ours. I didn't want to raise babies to have them killed. I was the last person in the world to be a livestock farmer.

Putting Nasty and Cheap by themselves in the dog paddock, so that I could give her some extra feed without it being gobbled up by the others, I went into the kitchen, but couldn't settle to anything, and decided to go to Chichester. I left a note for Gerald on the table, telling him I had gone shopping. I was doing what I always did when I felt depressed, setting off to buy new clothes.

The journey over the Downs at Goodwood lifted my spirits a little. In Chichester I left the car in a little central car park, and walked along past the Cathedral, heading for the Army & Navy Stores.

The street was busy, and as I waited for a gap in the traffic so that I could cross the road, I saw Conor on the other side. He didn't notice my half-raised hand, as he put his arm round the shoulders of the striking, black haired woman beside him and turned into a hotel. Having crossed the road I glanced through the window as I passed and saw him and the woman, laughing together at the bar. Now why should this make me feel

161

lonely and even more depressed?

Suddenly I didn't want to buy any clothes. Why would I want new clothes? These days all I wore were jeans, shirts and jumpers. There was no point in dressing up for animals which just plastered you with mud and hairs. I wasn't sure what I wanted.

I turned round and marched back past the hotel without turning my head, and spent the next half hour in Hammick's book shop, buying books I couldn't really afford, before treating myself to a cream tea.

Then, suddenly riddled with guilt at having walked out on Gerald in a bad temper, I raided Marks and Spencer's food department for something exotic to feed him that evening, and set off for home.

He was still working on the calving pen and hadn't even realised I had been into Chichester. Having read my note he had assumed that I had gone up to the shop in the village. He'd made himself a cup of coffee and gone back to work.

I tried to put the possible fate of Nasty's babies to the back of my mind. I would face the problem when it arose. Maybe they could be found pet homes. There must be other people with grass that needed mowing. One thing I was very sure of was that they would not end up in our freezer.

CHAPTER NINETEEN

I needn't have worried about explaining the unplanned pregnancy to Erica. She thought it was hilarious. And as she had been the only mother Cheap and Nasty had known, she reckoned that the lambs would qualify for the title of her grandchildren - which meant a small celebration was in order.

She arrived with some wine for us, and a chocolate cake for Cheap and Nasty, and the four of us had a picnic in the paddock. Quite a short picnic, as the only place to put down the tray of goodies was on the tank at the end of the water trough, well within reach of the two sheep. We didn't really mind them knocking the cake onto the ground, but only a flying catch from Erica saved the Gevrey Chambertin.

"That was a really good year," she said as she rose from her knees with the bottle held aloft.

Red wine doesn't really go with chocolate cake. It didn't seem to bother my sister, but the idea of supper that evening left me feeling a bit queasy. There was obviously a fundamental difference between Erica's and my genetic make up; she could coolly down a bottle of wine without turning a hair, whilst I ended up red in the face and feeling a little unsteady after two glasses.

"Good luck with the lambing," she called from the car window as she left. "You know where I am if you want any help."

She had left me with a list of essential equipment for Nasty's 'lying in', and I studied it as she clattered over the cattle grid and turned out of the drive.

Lubricating jelly to smear on my hands and arms, to enable their insertion into Nasty to unravel tangled lambs. Antibiotic spray for navels of newborn lambs. Heat lamp for reviving weak lambs. Bottles and teats for rearing orphan lambs, in case Nasty died! This last was unlikely as Nasty had never done anything helpful yet. Warm clothing and flask of coffee, with brandy.

"They always lamb in the middle of the night, when it's freezing cold," she'd said.

"Damn you, Henry!" I muttered.

Two weekends later I eased Nasty out of the field gate to eat her extra feed. If I fed her in the field she had to fight Cheap for the bucket. Our little celebration seemed to have convinced him that he was pregnant too.

I placed the feed under her nose and gave Cheap a handful of ewe and lamb nuts over the fence. Then, pulling up my coat collar against an unseasonably chilly wind, I turned back to Nasty and found that she was just sniffing at the bucket with a faraway expression in her eyes.

"What's the matter?" I asked her, and checked to see if the sheep nuts had gone mouldy.

Nasty gave me a vague stare, then walked across the yard and into the end of the hay barn. She stopped beside the hay so I pulled her down a handful. She sniffed it, then turned her head away, arched her back, and pushed slightly.

As it dawned on me that she was in labour, she lay down and refused to get up. This was where she had decided to produce her lambs; a week early by my reckoning.

Gerald had gone into town to the agricultural merchant to buy a water trough for his new calving pen, and I was on my own again.

Nasty was lying in an open area, barely under the barn roof, and it was a miserable grey day, with a cold east wind carrying occasional drops of rain. I tried to make her get up so that I could get her to a more sheltered part of the barn. But she hardly registered that I was there; her concentration on her contracting uterus was total.

Using the wheelbarrow I carted some straw bales to the barn and built a wind break around her while my mind was casting round the house, trying to remember where I had last seen Gerald's book on lambing. My hands were filthy, and I needed to scrub up and fetch all my equipment if I was to assist her with the birth. Stacking the last two bales into the gap so that she was totally enclosed and snug, I started to leave for the house. Nasty had other ideas.

She gave a strong, groaning, heave with her top lip stuck in the air, and ended with a little 'whickering' baa to her unborn lamb. I climbed over the bales and knelt on the straw to check her rear end, and found there were two tiny cloven hooves emerging.

Heart pounding, I tried to work out whether they were front feet the right way up, or back feet the wrong way up.

"Please God, let there be a head," I prayed.

God was listening. At the next heave a nose appeared, and two hefty pushes later a long thin, slippery, sodden lamb slid out onto the straw. It sneezed and shook its head, wet floppy ears slapping together. Nasty leapt to her feet, 'whickering' with excitement, and began to lick it dry.

I tried to wipe round its nose and mouth with a handful of straw, but Nasty pushed me out of the way, and I sat back on a bale and watched the miracle.

"You clever girl, Nasty," I crooned, "it's beautiful." I stretched out a hand to the lamb. Nasty glared at me and dared me to touch it, then placed herself between me and her baby.

The lamb struggled and half rose on ridiculously long legs. At the second attempt it managed to stand, but collapsed again onto its chin in an ungainly heap, as its back legs overtook the front ones when it tried to walk.

I realised Gerald was back when I heard the tractor start up down the hill. He and Steve had built a new lean-to down in the bottom yard for the tractor, so that Gerald could work on re-furbishing 'Fergie' under cover.

I wondered vaguely where he was going - not far, apparently. There was a crack and splintering of wood. The tractor engine cut out and the sound was replaced by a stream of invective from Gerald. Not a good time to tell him about Nasty, I decided.

The lamb lurched to its feet again, managed to lock its joints and wobbled towards its mum. But just as it was pushing underneath her in the direction of its first meal, she lay down and began to work towards providing it with a brother or sister.

With Nasty's mind now on other things, I got up to check the sex of the lamb. It was a ewe. I ran to the house to wash my hands, and collect the spray can of antibiotic from the cupboard in the scullery.

Gerald was already back in the kitchen and using the phone. He was talking to Ernie about tractors and didn't notice me come in. Nor did the dogs, because they were not there! Gerald had left the door unlatched again. I ran as fast as I could back to the barn, yelling for the dogs, convinced they were murdering the lamb.

They were sniffing around the bales when I got there, but hadn't quite worked out how to get in with Nasty. She was so used to them she didn't find them enough of a threat to stop producing her second child and deal with them.

I put the dogs safely away in their paddock with Cheap, and went back to Nasty, just in time for the arrival of the ewe lamb's twin brother. Both babies favoured their mother, having pretty speckled faces, instead of plain black like Henry's.

Using a bale as a seat - sitting on a straw bale is a surprisingly warm and pleasant experience - I picked up the ewe lamb, sat her on my lap and sprayed her navel. She nibbled at the side of my face as I did so, then pulled her head back and stared into my eyes with a quizzical and knowing expression. I was finding it hard to realise that this bright-eyed little woolly person had been but a rolling lump inside Nasty twenty minutes earlier.

Putting her down, I sprayed the navel of the other one, which Nasty was busily licking dry, then sat back on the straw bale again to watch. I had been sure there would only be two lambs, but I could be wrong.

The ewe lamb made another attempt at getting some food, and I tried to help her to latch on to a teat, but Nasty was not happy about the interference. It didn't take long for the lamb to manage without my assistance, and soon it was sucking noisily away, tail wagging furiously. I sat watching, and marvelling at the instinct-driven competence of Nasty and the lambs. Nasty hadn't read any books on 'lamb-birth'. She knew exactly what to do...and so did they.

A gust of wind through the open-ended barn reminded me how chilly it was. I had to get this small family somewhere warmer. The stable would be the best place, as I could hang a heat lamp in there. Removing my warm bottom from the straw bale, I collected the dogs and went back to the house, to get Gerald to help me move Nasty and the babies.

He looked up from the drawings of his plan for a bigger and better cattle shed, so that we could bring the Primroses in for the winter.

"Oh, there you are. Where have you been?" he said.

"Come and see."

"What? Come where? I can't come anywhere at the moment; I'm waiting for Ernie."

"Well, you can wait just as easily outside."

He hesitated, looking embarrassed. I didn't want to know what he had done with the tractor, and I sensed that he didn't want me to find out.

"Why don't you go out for the afternoon, get yourself something nice," he said, fishing in his pocket and handing me a twenty-pound note. What on earth had he done this time? I found I was becoming intrigued in spite of myself. Then I remembered Nasty.

"Just come with me a moment," I urged. "I need your help."

"Where to?" he asked suspiciously.

"The barn."

He looked relieved. You couldn't see the tractor shed from the barn.

"Why?"

"I want you to give me a hand. It won't take a minute."

Nasty was standing up when we arrived, but the lambs were not visible above the bales.

"Oh, what's wrong with that thing?" Gerald groaned. "Whatever it is, it's not worth a vet's bill."

Nasty glared at him over the top of the bales.

"I wish you wouldn't be so horrid about her – I'm sure she understands," I said. Nasty's eyes narrowed to yellow slits.

"Bloody thing looks mad to me. What's wrong with it?"

There was tiny bleat from one of the twins and Nasty instantly forgot Gerald and turned to deal with it. He stepped forward and peered over the bales.

"A lamb!...Where?...Two of them!.. When did this happen? Why didn't you call me, is she all right? Are they all right? Christ! - Lambs. Our first lambs...Ugly little buggers aren't they? They don't look a bit like Henry."

"Gerald, you can't mean that; they're absolutely beautiful. I saw them both born."

"Why didn't you call me to help?" he asked.

"There wasn't time, and Nasty didn't need help...anyway, what do you know about lambing?"

"I've read the book too."

A lamb struggled to its feet and stood there wobbling. In spite of himself, Gerald smiled.

I explained that I needed him to help me get them into the stable.

"You carry one, I'll bring the other one and Nasty."

"They're all wet and sticky." Gerald wrinkled up his nose and put his hands defensively in his pockets. I found a sack and wrapped it round the ewe lamb. He took it gingerly, holding it well away from his clothes.

"Come on you lot; let's get you somewhere warmer," I said, pulling some bales aside to let Nasty out, and picking up the other lamb.

Nasty panicked; with the lambs lifted off the floor she couldn't see where they had gone, and began a frantic search for them. Gerald had walked on ahead without realising I had a problem.

I called Nasty, who took no notice and continued to push bales of straw over in her desperate hunt for the missing children. I put my lamb down in the yard and called Nasty again, but she wouldn't look at me. Finally, feeling very cruel, I pinched the lamb's ear and it bleated pitifully. Nasty came out of her temporary pen like a greyhound released from the traps.

Picking up the lamb, I set off after Gerald, but once her child was off the ground, she lost it again. We progressed slowly to the nursery pen, with the lamb having to be put down every few feet to make her follow.

"Where did you get to?" Gerald asked, as we arrived.

"It's a long and rather boring story," I said, settling the lambs in the corner where I could hang the heat lamp over them. Nasty concentrated on licking the smell of humans off them.

"I'm just going to get Nasty some hay," I told Gerald.

"I'll do it," he said quickly - too quickly, I thought, remembering the hay store was next to the new tractor shed.

"No," I insisted. "There's a special bale of soft hay I have been saving for this event."

"Well, tell me where it is," he said desperately.

"You can get her some water if you're so keen to help," I said, handing him a bucket and trying to keep a straight face.

I walked round the barn towards the hay store with Gerald hot on my heels.

"It's not as bad as it looks," he said, as the tractor

shed came into view.

"Isn't it?" I was trying not to laugh.

Gerald had backed the tractor into the front corner of its new shed, and smashed the post. The roof which the post had been supporting had dropped about four feet, and the only thing which stopped it from dropping the rest of the way to the ground was the fact that it had come to rest on the tractor.

"You know," I said, "if I lent you a frock, you could go and take that 'Tractor driving for the Farmer's Wife' course."

"There's something wrong with the steering," he mumbled, "Ernie's going to have a look at it when we've put the roof back."

Ernie's van came down the drive as I went back to the house to collect the heat lamp for the twins. When I had the small family all settled and snug, I phoned Erica to tell her she was a granny.

"Congratulations," she said. "I'll come over and we'll wet the babies' heads."

I suggested she left it for a couple of days. I needed a clear head in case Nasty had any complications; and a slight sense of loyalty prompted me into a mild cover-up of Gerald's latest tractor accident. With luck, by Monday the tractor shed roof would be repaired.

CHAPTER TWENTY

In two days Nasty's babies were steady on their feet and bouncing around.

"We really should have my parents to stay, now we've got some baby animals to show them. Mum would love those two," said Gerald, watching the lambs as they jumped on and off a bale placed to block the draught from a hole in the stable wall.

The invitation to Gerald's parents was overdue and, as the rats seemed to have deserted the farm for the summer, it really was time they came. Especially if it meant that Gerald would look more kindly on Nasty's children; then it would be worth it...just.

They arrived the following weekend, after four days of unrelenting rain.

"I've brought my wellies," said Mary archly, as she climbed out of the car waving a transparent plastic carrying case containing a very new-looking pair of short white wellington boots.

"Good; you'll need those, I'm afraid. The farm is a bit of a quagmire at the moment," I said.

"I can see that," she said, looking with distaste at a few lumps of mud which had dropped from the tractor wheels onto the otherwise clean tarmac drive.

"I'll leave my boots in the car," said Arnold. They were an oddly matched pair; she short, rotund and rather fussily dressed in a pink suit with a frilly white blouse, while he towered above her, lean and slightly stooped, wearing a blazer and grey flannels. He was a gentle soul and, though very different in character, these two seemed to have a happy and stable marriage.

Arnold heaved a suitcase out of the boot while he looked round the yard.

"Where's Gerald? Thought the lad would be here to welcome us." There was still a trace of his Lancashire accent left, though he'd lived most of his adult life in London.

As if on cue, the tractor came trundling up the hill from the bottom yard, and for a moment I was guilty of the unworthy thought that Gerald had been waiting for this moment to make a dramatic entrance. They were very impressed.

We went indoors, driving off the welcoming dogs, but not before Huggy had laddered Mary's tights.

"Never mind, dear, can't be helped. You expect this sort of thing in the country," she said.

I showed them up to their room while Gerald put the coffee on, something he very rarely did. Mary looked at the new curtains which I had quickly made for the guest room, in honour of their visit.

"While I'm here, dear, I'll just let down the hem on that right-hand curtain for you. It's a bit shorter than the other one."

Mary always did things *for you*. It seemed to be her way of keeping one deeply indebted for the smallest assistance.

"That's very kind of you. I did make them in rather a hurry," I said.

"I don't expect you have a lot of time, with all the things you farmers' wives have to do. Feeding the chickens, collecting eggs, preserving fruit, baking bread and so on."

Dear God, was she expecting freshly baked bread?

I agreed that I did have to spend quite a lot of time

173

with the animals.

"Don't you have a man to look after them?" asked Arnold.

"Well, we do have Ernie on Wednesdays. This used to be his farm, but now he lives up in the village; and we did borrow one of my sister's farm hands to help with shearing the sheep," I said. "And of course Gerald does some of the jobs which are too heavy for me." Anything over a half hundredweight, I thought.

Arnold turned from hanging a brand new waxed jacket in the wardrobe.

"You mean he does a full day's work in London, then comes home and runs the farm? He always was a hard worker. I can see you're proud of him, Jill."

"Can you?...er...I mean, yes, yes, I am. I'll leave you to unpack. There's coffee downstairs." The smell of brewing coffee was beginning to drift through the house.

The kitchen seemed rather empty, until I realised the dogs weren't there.

"I put them out in their paddock," said Gerald. "Mum's not used to animals. In fact, it might be an idea to shut the dogs in the bottom yard stable for the next couple of days. It's not going to hurt them."

It probably wouldn't, I thought; wondering how Gerald and his parents would cope with two days and nights of non-stop howling.

After coffee I moved the dogs down to the stable where, instead of howling, they embarked on a rat hunt in the straw and rolled enthusiastically in the remains of an old cow-pat, setting the seal on their banishment from the house for the rest of the weekend.

Gerald suggested we all went out to see the lambs. Mary, in her new white wellingtons, paused on the doorstep and held a hand to her hair.

"It's a bit windy, Arnold," she said. "Can you pop upstairs and fetch my headscarf?"

As we waited at the back door for Arnold to return, Mary put her head on one side and listened.

"I can hear a bell. Is there a church nearby?" she asked.

I, too, could hear a bell. Bong...Bong...a pause, then Bong...Bong. It seemed to be coming from Nasty's stable.

Gerald had very quickly started calling her babies 'the terrible twins', convinced that they would take after their mother in character, and they were beginning to prove him right. Their favourite game at the moment was 'king of the castle', which they had started playing on a bale which I had put in the stable to exclude a draught. But now that they were bigger, I had put in some more bales, to give them a better adventure playground.

There was a hectic sound of straw rustling as we reached the stable. Then both lambs paused to stare at the human faces peering over their door, but they were too full of themselves to stand still for long.

"Look what we can do," they said, and raced off round the stable. The first one leapt onto a bale. As the second one arrived, the first took a flying leap at the metal shade of the heat lamp which swung against the wall... Bong. The second lamb waited for the lamp to swing back, then launched its shoulder against it. Bong... the lamp tolled sonorously.

Nasty watched them indulgently, quietly munching on a mouthful of hay, before turning her attention to Mary, who had unlatched the stable door and walked in to stroke the lambs, probably influenced by some muzzy memory of 'pets' corner' at the zoo. Nasty stopped chewing, some wisps of hay still hanging out of her mouth.

I kept an eye on her, as Mary reached out a hand to one of the lambs, which bucked away and galloped round behind its mother. Nasty stamped a front foot at Mary, and ducked her head menacingly. I took hold of a fistful of wool at the back of her neck, hoping to throw her off balance if she did charge.

Mary didn't notice as she headed for the other lamb. It dodged her hand and leapt onto the bales. From that height it studied her, nose to nose. Just as it seemed Mary was beginning to find its penetrating gaze a little disconcerting, the lamb, its power over the human established, jumped across onto another bale and flew off the top. Bong…went the shade against the wall, and Mary, trying to get away from the flying lamb, was hit by the lamp on its back-swing.

Arnold had noticed Nasty's expression and my grip on the wool.

"I think you'd better come out now, dear; they seem a bit excited."

"They're so sweet," said Mary, somewhat unnerved by these small creatures who should have been cuddly, but weren't.

"Any cake?" baa-ed Nasty.

"No, not at the moment," I said.

"What, dear?" said Mary.

"I was just telling Nasty I didn't have any cake for her. It's her favourite food."

"Oh, I see." she glanced at Arnold, who shrugged his shoulders slightly. I pretended I hadn't seen this exchange. Perhaps Gerald was right. Talking to sheep could well be one of the first signs of madness.

It was coming on to rain quite heavily again - this summer must have been coming near to a record for rainfall - so Mary decided they would put off going to see the cows until the next day. I left Gerald to entertain them while I took the dogs for a walk they didn't really want. Dachshunds aren't too keen on rain, unless they are hunting something, in which case they wouldn't notice a monsoon.

They made a big production of rolling about in the straw when I put them back in the stable, then lay around panting from the exertion of drying themselves. I fed them, and shut the top door before leaving, as the rain was gusting into the stable.

We went down to the Royal Oak for a meal that evening, and as we turned into the car park, we passed Conor's Land Rover coming out. He caught my eye, and winked. Why would Conor wink at me?

By the time we had parked and walked into the pub, I'd convinced myself that I had imagined it, until Gerald said: "Did that Irish bloke wink at you just now?"

"Ooh!...Have you got an admirer?" asked Mary.

"No, don't be silly," I said. "Of course he didn't - why on earth would he wink at me? He thinks I'm a nuisance, the dogs worry his pheasants and he's told me in no uncertain terms to stick to the footpaths through the woods. Now, shall we sit over there in the corner by the fireplace?"

The following morning Mary decided to re-do the hem on the spare bedroom curtain, the unevenness of which had obviously been worrying her as she drank her morning cup of tea. Gerald asked his father if he would like to help him with some work on the tractor, but Arnold decided he would rather give me a hand with the animals. The day was blustery, but at least it had stopped raining.

I wanted to keep the sheep in their well-grazed field for a few more days, to let the grass in the next field grow a little higher before turning them in there, so they needed some hay.

I grasped the handles of the wheelbarrow to fetch the hay from the barn, but Arnold said we could easily carry a bale between us, no need for the barrow. Together we lifted the heavy bale down from the stack, and an awkward journey ensued. Arnold's extra height meant that I was carrying most of the bale's weight, whilst the constant jolting as he skipped about, trying to avoid the worst of the mud, put considerable strain on my shoulder. It was a relief when we reached the field gate.

I cut the string, and as the bale naturally separated into segments, Arnold took one and proceeded to sprinkle it around him in delicate handfuls, while the sheep raced about trying to catch the stalks before the wind took them away. I sent him off with a section of the bale to give to Nasty, and went to fetch a bucket of ewe and lamb nuts for her.

He was just leaving the stable to refill her water bucket as I arrived.

"Who was that?" Nasty baa-ed, staring through the half open door after Arnold.

"Gerald's father," I told her, and she flashed him one of her 'looks' before turning to her feed. I gave both lambs a quick cuddle which excited them into a short period of 'bell ringing' practice.

When we got back indoors Mary got Arnold to re-hang the bedroom curtain, which she had altered very professionally.

"There, dear, doesn't that look better?" she said. And it did.

Gerald took them both down to look at the cows, while I prepared lunch, and half an hour later they returned, looking slightly stunned.

"They're so big, dear," Mary said. "I had no idea cows were so large...and such an interesting colour. I thought cows were black and white."

"How now brown cow?" said Arnold.

"Pardon, dear?"

Gerald took out the Primroses' pedigrees and began to explain them to his parents, who until that point had not realised that all the cows were called Primrose. This confused them terribly; it was no good them looking at me, I was still trying to work out the reasoning behind it as well.

The rain, which had held off until lunch time, returned with a vengeance, putting paid to a promised afternoon walk around the farm, although I don't think Mary had been all that keen on the idea. As she said, you can see nearly all of it from the upstairs windows. They decided not to stay for a second night and set off for home around mid-afternoon, promising to come and see us again when the weather was better.

After waving them off, I went down to the bottom yard to rescue the dogs from their prison, expecting an ecstatic welcome. They were all sound asleep in the warm straw, and none too keen to brave the rain to come home.

"You must," I told them. "If you create this sort of a precedent Gerald will have you out here permanently. No more winters in front of the Aga."

Gerald came down the hill on the tractor, drove slowly past the cows' field, studying them, then rolled into the yard and parked quite competently in the newly repaired tractor shed. I would like to have congratulated him on his improved handling of 'Fergie' but thought he might think I was being patronising. In the end I said nothing.

"Hello, dogs," he said; and, to me: "Won't be long now."

"What won't?"

"The gingery coloured Primrose, number 58...the one you call Hippo."

"What?...Calving, you mean? She's not due till September."

"No, August. I worked it out again when I was showing them to Mum and Dad. I must get some calving equipment." He walked away down the yard to inspect the new pen in which this momentous event was to take place.

I paused at the cows' field on the way back up the hill with the dogs. Hippo was enormous, but didn't look unduly bothered by the fact. In the few moments that I was watching them all four Primroses relieved themselves. This is what cows seem to do best. On a still night, with the bedroom window open, and the cows in a field close to the house, the splatter of cow pats is an almost constant sound, interspersed with slightly less frequent Niagara Falls imitations.

I had managed to put the matter of calving to the back of my mind, but now I was having to bring it forward again...What did he mean by calving equipment? Surely the vet would have that. Still, Gerald had promised he would be here for the births. I didn't need to worry. A whine from Huggy reminded me that we were all getting wet.

CHAPTER TWENTY ONE

Gerald's bedside table began to groan under the weight of books on parturition - the cow variety - collected from Foyles bookshop in London, by the ever-helpful Hazel. Then one Saturday he returned from a shopping trip to the local agricultural merchants', carrying bags of antiseptic spray, lubricating jelly, calving ropes, a calving jack and a block and tackle.

As a female who has actually given birth, I was horrified by this array. The idea of having a baby hauled out of one with a jack, or, worse still, winched out using a block and tackle, smacked of medieval cruelty.

"Whatever happened to natural birth?" I asked.

"It's not always easy with these exotic breeds. They have huge calves."

I recalled a conversation in the pub a few months ago with the local vet. It was he who had referred to the South Devons as an exotic breed, but somehow the description didn't fit the enormous brainless Hippo, or her sister with the vacant stare, whom I had secretly named Gormless.

Gerald didn't know this and usually referred to the cows by their numbers; though, apart from resorting to the toothbrush and scrubbing out their ears to decipher them, I didn't really know whether he was putting the right number to the right cow.

He read books on calving every night, then had nightmares and talked in his sleep about neo-natal diseases, while I seriously considered a temporary move into the spare room before we both became nervous wrecks.

Hippo continued her unhurried round of daily existence unaware of the awful fate that could await her. She grazed, lay in the sun chewing cud, then, hauling her bulk up with an unattractive grunt, she grazed again. She showed no signs of imminent birth and Gerald and I relaxed a little.

He even spent two nights away at a conference in Harrogate. Although he rang both evenings to enquire after Hippo, it wasn't until I had put the phone down on the second call that I realised he hadn't asked me how I was.

That evening I stood in front of the full-length mirror in the bedroom, and studied the country version of me. In London I had managed to look reasonably smart, not as smart as Hazel, but then she was younger and slimmer, but I had certainly looked a whole lot better than the creature I now confronted.

The once carefully dressed long hair which I had worn in a 'french pleat', was now pulled back into a scruffy pony tail, secured by a thick elastic band courtesy of the post office - it had arrived round a bundle of letters. This elastic band was actually an emergency measure as the marginally more attractive black velvet one I usually wore had been eaten by one of Nasty's babies during a cuddling session.

Below the untidy hair were eyebrows which had grown straggly, above eyelids which could really do with at least a hint of shadow. I had gone past the age when I could get away without using make up.

My eyes ran down a once-white shirt, now stained lichen green from leaning against a field gate, to jeans with muddy paw marks on them up to knee level, and a tear just below the crutch, where I had misjudged the climb through a barbed wire fence, then on to feet clad in Gerald's socks with straw sticking to them.

This was not the woman he had married. It was no wonder he forgot the odd goodbye kiss as he left for work. I resolved to take my appearance in hand.

The next morning I managed to get an appointment with the hairdresser for 2.30 that afternoon, plus a much-needed manicure. When Gerald arrived home after his Harrogate trip, I would present him with the woman's magazine image of dutiful...beautiful?... wife wielding the cocktail shaker, the delicious smell of food wafting from the kitchen.

I took the dogs for a quick walk down the farm track before starting preparations for a really special evening meal. Today was going to be devoted to me and Gerald.

Three of the Primroses were lying peacefully near the field gate...Hippo was standing in the far corner of the field under a large holly tree. Strange...they were always together. I called to her, but she took no notice. I don't know why I had expected her to, she never had before.

Cursing her for deciding to behave oddly today of all days, I walked across the field for a closer look, not sure what I would be looking for when I got there.

She glanced at me, then returned to staring over the fence. I tried to drive her back to the others, but she only moved a few steps, then swung back towards the holly tree. As she turned away I noticed a slight discharge from her rear end.

"Not today," I groaned. Hippo looked round at her side and raised her tail slightly as she strained.

There was a moment of blank shock, then my brain

kicked in. I must get her into the calving pen. First I must put the dogs away.

When I looked round they were halfway across the field heading for Conor's wood. "NO!" My hysterical bellow shocked them into hesitation, allowing me just long enough to shorten the distance between us to the dachshund equivalent of just before the 'point of no return'. They stopped, looking sheepish, and I put their leads on. That was my last bit of luck that day.

With the dogs safely shut indoors, I ran back to the bottom yard and opened the gate to the calving pen, then ran up to the field. Hippo was still standing up, thank goodness.

The other Primroses were lying down so I left the gate open, and tried to drive Hippo down the field; every time I had just got her moving, she circled me and returned to the holly tree where she had decided to give birth. It was warm and sheltered and really quite a sensible place - but it wasn't what Gerald had planned.

Dashing to the feed shed I got a plastic bucket of cattle cake, to see if this would tempt her out. Hippo showed no interest at all in food, which wasn't really surprising, but the other three rose to their feet and joined us, one Primrose shoving her head into the bucket with such force that she pushed it out of my hand. By the time they had all fought over it - except Hippo - the bucket was split from top to bottom, and minus its handle.

I decided to drive all of the cows into the calving pen, then put three back in the field. The others started down the field under my urging, but Hippo still wouldn't move. I pushed the cows on, hoping she would follow, but to her we didn't exist.

Shutting them in the bottom yard, I collected a stick

and went back to her. It was no good; all she did was circle me. I needed help.

"Would you be wanting some help?"

The voice from just behind me shot my stomach into my throat.

"Sorry, didn't mean to be making you jump. You seemed to be having a bit of trouble with that cow. Looks as if she's calving."

"Conor...I. er, yes, yes, I think she is and I can't get her away from here. She's supposed to do it in the new calving pen in the bottom yard. Yes, please, I would like some help. Thank you. Do you know about calving?"

"I grew up on a farm in Donegal. We had a house cow."

With Conor on one side and me on the other, we slowly managed to keep Hippo in a straight line, and ease her out of the field, down the track and into the calving pen. She walked across to the corner and lay down, half rolling over as she pushed again.

"How long has she been pushing?" he asked.

"I don't know...she was doing it when I found her. Do you think I should get the vet?"

"She'll probably be all right, but it wouldn't hurt to be on the safe side...I have to go now, good luck."

"Thank you, thank you so much, I couldn't have got her in without you." Something inside me screamed 'don't leave me'.

"No problem," he said as he climbed out through the bars of the pen. I watched his easy stride as he crossed the field to the wood. He didn't look back.

"Vet," I said to myself. Opening the yard gate, I pushed the other three cows away from the stacked hay, where they had already pulled down three bales, and drove them back to their field on my way up to the house.

First I rang Gerald, so that he could be on his way.

"She's calving; you've got to come home quickly. I don't know how long she's been straining."

"What?"

"It's me...Hippo...she's calving. Come home."

"Just a moment." He said something to Hazel in the background, then: "Are you sure? I thought it usually happened at night."

"Yes, I am...and Conor said she was, too."

"What's he doing there?"

"He's not now, he just helped me get her in. Gerald please come home, you promised you would. I can't cope with this myself."

"Calm down, you're getting hysterical. Cows have calves all the time."

This last remark, after all his nightmares, rendered me speechless for a moment. He was talking to Hazel again.

"Jill...I'm very busy at the moment, and have a meeting in half an hour. I'm sure she'll be all right. You phone the vet and I'll try to get home a bit earlier. Ring me if anything happens."

"Something is happening," I screeched, but he'd rung off.

I dialled the vet's number. The receptionist told me that the farm animals' specialist in the practice was out doing a caesarean on another cow, but she would get Mr Coliffe, the small animals' vet, to pop out and have a look.

A rambler in an orange jacket and red woolly hat walked past the kitchen window, studying an Ordnance Survey map, and turned onto the footpath towards the

Barrington-Smythes' cottage.

"Triffic," I muttered to the dogs as I pulled on my wellingtons before going back to Hippo.

She was lying down in the darkest corner of the pen and groaned at me when I spoke to her. It slowly dawned on me that the vet might want to examine her properly. There was no question of getting her into the crush, even if it had been large enough.

I dragged a metal gate into the pen and roped one end of it to the rails about three feet from the corner, then put a halter on Hippo, but she got up and swung away from me before I managed to loop up the trailing lead rope, which she then dragged round the floor and trod into a cow pat.

I heard the vet's car draw up in the top yard and shouted to him to come on down the hill. He drove carefully down the bumpy track into the bottom yard, got out and opened the car boot.

He took off his shoes, and pulled on green plastic thigh boots, donned a matching apron, then came creaking and slapping across the yard to the pen.

"Right! What have we got here then?" he said. "My goodness, that's a big cow."

"She seems to be in labour. I don't know what stage; I've never calved a cow before and I don't know how long she's been straining. I'd feel happier if you'd have a look."

I wasn't sure if I would...with his fair curly hair and round pink face he looked about sixteen, and wasn't exuding the kind of confidence I needed at that moment.

"Will she tie up?" he asked.

"I don't know' I was lucky to get the halter on her, but she got away before I could tie the rope round her neck."

He looked at the filthy end of the rope.

"Can you fetch a bucket of warm water and a towel?" he asked.

Now this was something I could manage, and I set off up to the house, vaguely noting that the hill was not as steep as it used to be. I must be getting fitter.

"Good," he said, when I got back. "Now, you were going to get her behind that gate, I presume." He seemed to be weighing up the safety aspects of my makeshift crush.

Between us we drove Hippo into the corner and the vet allowed *me* to tie the rope to the rail. It was slippery with cow muck, and Hippo kept throwing her head about. By the time the rope was secured, I had dung up to my elbows and spattered across my face from the flicking rope end.

I remembered I hadn't cancelled my appointment with the hairdresser.

"OK, you come and lean on the gate and keep her pinned there," he said, as he pulled on a long plastic glove and soaped his hand and arm.

"Right. Got her?" he asked, poised behind the cow like a bullfighting banderillero about to plant a dart.

"I think so." My feet were slowly sliding across the floor as Hippo pushed against the gate.

He slipped his arm into the cow and groped about for a minute or two...then withdrew it.

"That seems all right – it's the right way round, and not too big."

"When is she likely to calve?"

"Oh, I should think in the next six hours or so," he said, stripping off the plastic glove and handing it to me. I dropped it over the rails into a wheelbarrow.

Back in the house, I phoned the hairdresser, who

couldn't give me another appointment for a week. As I replaced the phone it rang. It was Gerald.

"What's Hippo doing? - God, now you've got me calling her Hippo. I wish you wouldn't give the animals silly names."

"It makes the whole thing slightly more bearable," I said. "She's not doing anything much. The vet says she's all right and should calve in the next six hours. Have you finished your meeting? Can you start home now? You want to be here for the birth of your first calf, don't you?"

"Er, yes," he said. "I've got to go now, but I'll try to get away as soon as I can."

I phoned Erica for some moral support.

"Hippo has gone into labour," I said. "Do you know anything about calving?"

"Not really; you'd better speak to Donald, he's around somewhere. I'll give him a call."

There was a silence, somewhere in the distance a door closed, then Donald picked up the receiver.

"Hi, hear you've got a calf on the way. What's the problem?"

"Well, nothing really. I just feel that the vet has a rather 'laid back' attitude to the whole business, and I'm not really sure what I should be looking for."

"Which vet is it?"

"Mr. Coliffe."

"Isn't he the small animals' man in that practice? I thought you had 'whatsisname' for the cows."

"We do, but he's out."

"OK. How long has she been in labour?"

"I don't know. She'd already started when I found her in the field." I looked at my watch. An unbelievable three hours had passed since I had first noticed Hippo under the holly tree.

"Is she straining?"

"No more than she was three hours ago."

"She ought to be getting on with it a bit faster than that. Have you got any help? Where's Gerald?"

"In London. He's beginning to give me the impression that he would rather not be here until it's all over."

"Well, give it another couple of hours, then if she's still not getting on with it I would get the vet back again. Do you want me to come over?"

Yes, said my head, but my mouth said: "No...I won't drag you all the way over here. It's not your problem, but thanks for the advice."

"Good luck," he said.

I half-heartedly set about preparing the evening meal, then left it. I couldn't concentrate. I made a flask of coffee, pushed a packet of ginger biscuits into my jacket pocket and went down to the bottom yard.

Hippo looked at me with a haggard expression. I wondered how she managed to turn that dull lump of a face into any expression, but Hippo definitely looked haggard.

"It's all right, petal, soon you'll have a beautiful baby."

Hippo groaned.

"All right then, an ugly one, just like his mummy." I suddenly hated myself for this remark, and tried to justify it by thinking, it's only a cow after all. But it wasn't - it was Hippo, and she was in pain. I felt a twinge in the pit of my stomach. Oh no! Now I was getting sympathetic labour pains.

I sat on a straw bale for an hour, watching Hippo's flanks ripple with contractions which didn't seem to become any stronger. The twittering of sparrows in the rafters was the only sound in that quiet afternoon. Convinced that something was wrong and she should have been further forward by now, I went back to the house and phoned the vet.

"Well, if you're really worried, I could come out again," he said reluctantly.

"I am. My brother-in-law said something a bit more positive should be happening by now."

"Ah, your brother-in-law." I began to go off this pussy cat vet.

"Yes. He's a farmer, and knows what he's talking about."

"I've just got something to finish off here. I'll be with you in about an hour. OK?"

"It will have to be," I said ungraciously.

I rang London to check that Gerald was on his way home. He wasn't. Something had come up, Hazel said, but he would get home as soon as possible.

I refilled the flask, let the dogs into the garden for ten minutes, then returned to Hippo. The vet arrived half an hour later.

"Right. Let's have her up and behind the gate again."

We forced poor Hippo onto her feet and trapped her behind the gate and the vet embarked on another internal examination. He took longer this time, and his expression changed from slightly supercilious to worried. Finally he withdrew his arm and turned to me looking embarrassed.

"I'm afraid it's dead. We'll never get it out through there; we'll have to do a caesarean."

"Dead! What d'you mean, dead? It can't be...why?...Gerald will go mad. Why is it dead? You said it was all right when you checked her."

"I'm sorry," he said. "Excuse me a moment, I'll have to use the car phone to get someone else out to help me do the caesar." He left, half running, towards his car.

I stared at Hippo, she moved and her udder swung. Dear God, she had an udder full of milk and nothing to feed it to, somebody was going to have to milk her. How did they do a caesarean on a cow? Gerald was going to go mad, this calf was by one of the country's top bulls and worth a small fortune. How could it be dead, and, what was more important, why?

The vet came back, though he would obviously rather have been miles away.

"Why did it die?" I asked.

"I don't know. We'll know better when we've got it out."

"How do you do a caesar? Should I get some clean straw in here?"

"No, this is all right. We give her a local jab and cut a cross in her side. We do it with her standing up."

There was an awkward silence.

"I'll get another cup if you'd like some coffee," I said.

He nodded and I escaped to the house and stayed there until the second vet came down the drive.

He was the proper farm vet. He quickly pulled on a glove, soaped his arm and inserted it carefully into poor Hippo.

"We've got a torsion here," he said almost immediately.

"Torsion?" I asked.

"Yes - the uterus has swung round and twisted the neck of the womb, like a twisted sleeve...there's no way the calf could have come out through there."

"Would that have been obvious earlier on?" I asked, looking at the 'pussy cat' vet, who was busy not looking at me.

"Well, probably," said the cow vet, suddenly realising life might have been simpler if he had thought before he had spoken. "We may not have to do a caesar if I can swing the whole thing round again."

He began working inside the cow, and in a few minutes was sweating profusely.

"If that had been discovered earlier, could we have done a caesarean and saved the calf?" I was filled with anger at this upsetting and unnecessary waste of life.

"Possibly...it's difficult to...tell." His speech was somewhat fragmented by the effort he was putting in to trying to swing the uterus and calf back the right way. The other vet had hidden himself behind Hippo and was being very quiet.

Suddenly the cow vet grunted.

"Got it," he said, withdrawing his arm and wiping the sweat from his face with the other forearm. "Give me a minute, then we'll get ropes on it and get it out."

Poor Hippo had begun to strain in earnest now, but was too tired to deliver the calf herself. Ropes were attached to its front legs and head, and Hippo groaned and bellowed as her dead child was dragged from her. I realised that my shoulders were rigid from tension. The calf's head and shoulders appeared, then it jammed at the hips and had to be rotated to free them. Finally it was delivered. A fine bull calf - just what Gerald had wanted.

Between them the two vets lifted the calf's body over the fence onto the wheelbarrow, while I, idiotically, tried to shield this sight from Hippo. The pussy cat vet was packing his car and preparing to leave.

"What does one do about the milk?" I asked his colleague. "I can't milk a cow."

"Harry Soutar down the road has got some day-old calves; he might sell you one. At least she'd have something to look after. I'll hang on while you give him a ring if you like. It would be as well to give her something as soon as possible, so she'll accept it."

I dashed back up to the house and rang Gerald to give him the sad news, and ask if it would be all right to buy a calf, but Hazel said he was on his way home.

The decision had to be made quickly, so I made it, and rang Harry Soutar who said, yes, he had a calf, and would bring it round straight away.

He pulled up in the bottom yard about quarter of an hour later and opened the back of his van.

"Will this one do?" he asked. "He's hungry, he hasn't been fed since this morning."

A cheeky, perfectly beautiful, shiny brown and white calf looked out at me, legs still braced apart from keeping his balance in the van, and his small pink tongue protruding an inch or so.

"Yes," I said, feeling myself smile for the first time that day.

The vet smeared some of the birth fluids from the dead calf onto this baby before putting him into the pen behind Hippo, who was still tied up. I released her from the halter and she slowly turned round and stared at the calf. He stood four-square and stared back.

"Maa," he said.

Every fibre of Hippo's being was suddenly concentrated on him - she gave a moo which started in her socks, and rose to an almost inaudible squeak.

The calf smelled the milk and tried to reach her udder, but nature was telling Hippo to lick him clean and dry first. There followed a fairly rough battle of wills, but the calf's persistence finally won and she allowed him to feed for a minute or two, then she pushed him away as more contractions expelled the afterbirth.

The vet gave her two injections, and promised to come back in a couple of days to give her another.

"I'm sorry the result couldn't have been happier, but that's the way it goes sometimes," he said ruefully.

I thanked him for managing to avoid a caesar, anyway, as he collected his bag and walked off to the car, then I pushed the wheelbarrow with its sorry load round to the back of the barn. Gerald would have to bury it when he came home.

I had fetched hay and water for Hippo, and was leaning on the fence watching them when Gerald came into the yard. The calf said "Maa".

"It's born!" he said, walking fast across the yard. Before I could say anything he had seen the calf. "What on earth's that? It's a throwback, this is terrible... Jill, why didn't you phone me?"

"I've been phoning you all day, Gerald. That's not..."

"I'm going to ring Davidson in Devon. This isn't good enough, they must have used the wrong A.I. sperm. I want my money back. That cow was bloody expensive."

"Listen!" I yelled. "That is not Hippo's calf. Hippo's calf is dead. I've had a terrible day, so has she, and you wouldn't come home. I've done the best I can. I can't milk her, so the vet said get a calf."

"Dead! What d'you mean, dead? Why? Where is it?

195

What was it? Why is it dead? What happened?"

"Her uterus got twisted and it couldn't get out, and it died."

"Why didn't you get the vet earlier? You could have saved it; you could have made them do a caesarean or something. You know how much I wanted that first calf."

"I did get the vet - he said there was nothing wrong. Stop shouting at me...I've had enough." Suddenly I burst into tears and couldn't stop crying.

"Where is it?"

"Round the back of the barn," I snivelled.

He came back after a few minutes, pushing the barrow and heading for the cattle crush.

"What are you doing?" I said through my handkerchief as I blew my nose.

"I'm going to weigh it."

"Why? It's dead Gerald. D.E.D. Dead."

"Don't make jokes. I bought this crush to weigh the stock and that's what I'm doing."

"Don't do this, it's crazy ...that calf is heavy, and I don't think I'm strong enough to help you get it back into the barrow. Put it back behind the barn and come in, have a drink and calm down...*I* could do with one."

I couldn't face cooking a meal, so we sat in front of the television with sandwiches and gin. After half an hour Gerald stopped railing against the world and incompetent vets and went quiet. I glanced at him to see tears in the corners of his eyes.

"I was really looking forward to that calf," he said.

That night, the tragedy brought us closer together than we had been for some time... until he told me my hair smelled of cow muck; by the time I had washed and dried it, he was asleep.

CHAPTER TWENTY TWO

The next morning Gerald woke early, sat up in the bed, and gave me a dig with his elbow.

"Double suckling!" he said.

"What?" I mumbled through my pillow. He had woken me out of a dream in which Conor had shot the pussy cat vet with his pistol, and was ordering me to bury him behind the barn, along with the dead calf. "I was having a nightmare," I said. Gerald wasn't interested.

"She's got gallons of milk. We'll get another calf from Soutar. She can easily rear two."

I didn't think this was a very good idea. Hippo was so besotted with her new child that she probably wouldn't accept another one...it was too late. Yesterday we might just have fooled her into thinking she'd had twins, but I thought even Hippo could count up to one.

Swallows were twittering on the telephone wire outside the bedroom window as they planned their autumn journey to Africa.

My tentative protests about getting another calf were brushed aside. Gerald was not in the mood to have me pour cold water on his brilliant idea. He got straight on the phone to Harry Soutar.

As a result of this call the van arrived in the yard half an hour later bearing a small black and white person, bawling for his breakfast. He was unloaded near to Hippo's pen, and she turned from cooing sweet nothings to her child. Her eyes widened slightly as she stared at the newcomer.

Gerald was busy paying Harry Soutar, who then said he was in a bit of a rush, and drove off, leaving Gerald struggling to hold onto a lively and hungry calf by the collar of orange baler twine it was wearing. The calf bawled for his mother, and coughed.

"You're strangling it," I said.

"Well, give me a hand then," he ground out as it bounced on his foot. "Open the gate."

"I don't think Hippo likes it." I looked at the cow who was standing very still. She glanced at her brown and white baby, lying in the corner of the pen, then returned to watching Gerald's struggles. The calf's hooves scraped on the concrete yard as it resisted Gerald with surprising strength.

"She'll love it...if I can just get it in there." He hauled on the string.

"Twist his tail and pull him with it; that's what they did with the other one yesterday."

Finally, between us we manoeuvered the calf to the gate of the pen, and shoved him through. Hippo took two strides and shoved him out again.

"Push him in. That stupid cow's in the way," said Gerald.

I drove Hippo back and Gerald pushed the calf in again. He smelled milk and dived towards Hippo's udder; she turned at speed, picked him up on her forehead, and hurled him against the back wall of the pen, which was the original stone wall of the barn.

He lay crumpled up at the foot of it in stunned surprise.

"Christ!" said Gerald.

"Get him out!" I screamed, as Hippo lined up for another go, tossing her head menacingly.

"No...she'll take to him in a minute, she just needs

time to get used to the idea."

"If that's how she gets used to the idea, there will be nothing left to 'take to' at the end of it." The brown and white baby was getting to his feet and threatening to get caught up in round two.

I leapt into the pen with a hastily snatched dung fork.

"Get him out, I can't hold her for long," I yelled at Gerald who still hadn't moved. Hippo didn't appear to be noticing the fact that I was prodding her with the sharp tines of the fork, and was trying to walk through me to the calf.

Gerald lost his temper and on his way across the pen, he punched Hippo in the face. She came as close as a cow is ever likely to come to baring her teeth at him, and I thanked God that South Devons are born without horns. Ignoring her, he pulled the calf out and I backed out after him, still jabbing her in the chest with the fork.

Hippo turned back to her brown and white baby with a low moo, and began to comb the hair on his head with a tongue like sandpaper.

"Now what?" Gerald said, as the calf lunged across the yard, bellowing and towing him, slipping and sliding behind.

"He's hungry," I said.

"I know he's bloody hungry...sodding stupid cow." This last remark was to Hippo who was still glaring at us. He looked at his watch. "I told Hazel I'd be in by eleven. I'm going to have to go."

"You can't leave me like this," I said.

"Look, we'll put him in that shed over there and...oh, I don't know, feed him or something. Get some milk powder, make him a bottle. I'll sort it out this evening when I come home."

He dragged the calf across the yard, and shut him in the lean-to shed where Ernie Challen had kept his calves. Ernie might have been some help at the moment, but I knew he was away visiting his sister; no doubt regaling her with the unorthodox farming habits of the latest tenants of Warren Hanger.

"I've got to go, see you later," Gerald flung back over his shoulder as he half ran up the hill.

I gave the calf a bucket of water to keep him amused, and went back up the hill. Gerald's car was just turning out of the drive as I reached the house. Letting the dogs out into the garden, I contemplated my next move over a cup of coffee, checking the milk situation in the fridge. Half a pint wasn't going to help much.

The only sensible thing to do was to lose face, by asking Harry Soutar to come and take the calf back. I knew Gerald wouldn't do this; he wasn't very good at admitting he had made a mistake.

The calf was hungry and I was being pushed towards a rapid decision by the deep-seated instinct in every female, that a hungry baby must be fed.

If Hippo wouldn't accept the calf, and I certainly wasn't prepared to try again, there was no good reason for keeping him. On this thought, I picked up the phone and dialled Harry Soutar's number.

He wasn't keen to have the calf back, but eventually agreed when I said he could keep half the money Gerald had paid for it - I wasn't looking forward to the evening.

To cheer myself up I went out to the paddock where Cheap, Nasty, and the lambs were lying in the morning sun. Quasi and Modo, named for their early bell ringing abilities, came up to see if I had brought them anything interesting. They shared their mother's love of chocolate, and a bourbon biscuit each made their day.

I sat for a while on the grass beside the recumbent Cheap, and told him about the morning's excitement, while he belched and chewed cud and looked wisely at me. It made me feel better.

Harry Soutar arrived and we loaded up the calf again.

"You should have tied her up and made her accept him," he said, as he reluctantly handed me back some of the money.

"You and your brilliant ideas, Gerald," I muttered under my breath, as I went in to phone Erica and tell her about the disastrous calving.

"I tried to get you yesterday," she said. "Then we had to go out. How did it go?"

I told her.

"You sound as if you could do with cheering up. Shall I come over? We could have lunch at the pub."

"That sounds like an excellent idea. Make it about one o'clock; that'll give me time to walk the dogs and get tidy...I was supposed to be at the hairdresser's yesterday, not spending my day in a bovine delivery ward."

"Hang on a sec. What was that, Donald? No...they lost it...Torsion. Yes. OK. You there, Jill?"

"Yes."

"Donald reckons it was that small animals vet's fault, she was in labour far too long. Anyway, see you about one o'clock."

The first person I saw when we walked out of the sunshine into the dark interior of the pub was Conor. He was just turning away from the bar with a couple of pint mugs in his hands. The slight, fair-haired man I had seen him with before was sitting at a table in the corner.

Conor paused in his journey across the room.

"How did it go?" he asked.

"We lost the calf. It was all rather sad."

"I'm sorry to hear that, but that's the way of things. Where you have livestock, you have dead stock."

I didn't find this a very comforting thought, and turned to introduce Erica to him, but she was already at the bar ordering drinks. He moved on over to his companion.

"Better luck next time," he said as he placed their drinks on the table.

I sat at a table for two, beside the window overlooking the green, and studied the hunting scenes on the curtain beside me, before pulling it further back to let a little more sunshine in.

"Who's that? The chap that spoke to you just now," said Erica, putting two large gin and tonics down on the table, whilst staring at Conor. I moved the drinks onto the mats.

"That's Conor, the mystery Irishman I told you about."

"He is 'drop dead' gorgeous."

"Not bad looking, I suppose," I said, in what I hoped was an offhand sort of way. My treacherous heart was thumping uncomfortably and I was confused, and slightly angry, at the effect this man was beginning to have on me. I was an adult, twice-married woman, not some fifteen-year-old girl.

"Put him down, Erica, you don't know where he's been - in fact, nobody around here knows where he's been. Well, apart from Donegal; he said he grew up there."

"A man of mystery, how intriguing," she said, still looking at him. Any minute he was going to look round and see her.

I passed her the menu from the centre of the table.

"What do you want to eat?...There's more written up on the blackboard over there, beside the fireplace."

"Is there a Mrs. Conor?" asked Erica.

"No...er, I mean, I don't know. He seems to live alone; nobody's ever mentioned a wife."

"Perhaps he's gay; that's probably his boyfriend. What a waste. Have you noticed how some of the sexiest actors on the telly are gay?"

"No...I mean, yes," I said. "But I don't think he's gay. I saw him with a very attractive woman in Chichester once. Anyway, could we talk about something else? He's going to notice you staring at him in a minute."

I told her about our efforts to persuade Hippo that 'double suckling' was a good idea, and she suggested we video our attempts at farming, then we could sell the result to all the agricultural colleges as an illustration of how not to farm. This was much too near the truth, and something only a close family member could get away with saying.

Conor and his friend left the pub after they had finished their pints, and sat in a dark blue Jaguar sports car chatting for a while, before Conor got out and walked across to his Land Rover. I studied his walk for any signs of a mincing gait.

"Now who's staring at him," said Erica.

We had finished our second cup of coffee, when Erica glanced at her watch.

"I'd better go," she said. "We've got a National Farmers Union meeting to go to this evening. Don't forget, we're only a phone call away if you get any more trouble."

"Don't wish any more on me," I said. "I don't think I'm cut out for farming."

"I'm sure Gerald will get sick of it if anything else goes wrong. He seems determined to learn the hard way," she said.

We went back to the farm where Erica refused the offer of another coffee, and left for home.

All in all, I reflected, her visit designed to cheer me up had not had the desired effect. It had left me wondering if Conor was gay, and confirmed my suspicion that other people were finding our efforts at farming highly amusing.

When Gerald came home that evening his first words were: "I suppose we'd better have another go at getting her to accept that calf. Did you feed it?"

"Sit down and eat your supper...I sent it back to Harry Soutar."

"Without asking me?"

"Obviously." There must have been something in my voice that warned him a row at this point was not a good idea.

"It was probably for the best, I suppose. We don't really want a farm full of mongrels," he said. I think he was secretly relieved that the decision had been taken away from him.

CHAPTER TWENTY THREE

I finally managed to get my hair trimmed and restyled; unfortunately it was the manicurist's day off, but as I was running out of fingernails for her to work on, it didn't really matter.

Walking out of the hairdresser's into the sunny afternoon, I felt the wave of confidence which a hairdo always imbues. A trip to 'Boots' for a new lipstick and the impulse buy of a summer dress completed the new me. I changed into the new dress in the shop, and arrived back in the village feeling pretty stunning.

Trouble was, apart from Margaret in the shop, there was nobody around to stun. She served me with some stamps and admired my new outfit, then as she came out from behind the post office counter she noticed something.

"Oh dear...he's forgotten his stamps, and he came in special."

She picked up a book of stamps from the ledge provided for customers to write on.

"Who has?" I said vaguely as I tried to decide which magazine to take from the rack. I had promised myself a civilised hour with a pot of tea and some light reading in the garden, before checking the animals and tackling the ironing, which was piling up in the spare bedroom.

"That Conor," she said.

Nerves in my stomach twitched. Should I offer to drop the stamps in on my way home? I had just decided 'definitely not', when Margaret turned to me.

"You couldn't possibly drop them in on your way home, could you, dear? He came up specially for them."

Could Margaret read minds? She had picked the words straight out of my head. Unnerved, I agreed to take them. At least for once I would be looking respectable when we met; and, after all, he had helped me with the cow. Surely it was the least I could do.

The car springs creaked as it bumped along the unmade track to Conor's cottage; a quick glance into the mirror to check my lipstick almost had me off the track into the ditch. I wrenched the wheel back, visions of me arriving at the cottage covered in mud and duckweed filling my mind. "Not this time," I said aloud through clenched teeth.

The Land Rover was parked on the grass in front of the cottage. Washing was moving gently on the clothesline running between the side of the house and an old apple tree near the pond. My eye ran idly along the shirts and underpants and stopped with a jolt at the black lace knickers and bra.

So much for Erica's theory that Conor was gay. Conor wasn't gay and I was a stupid married woman who was spending too much time alone. If he had been four feet tall with a squint and a limp, would I have been interested? Of course not – well, as long as he didn't have that soft Irish accent I wouldn't.

If I tell Erica about the washing she'll probably decide he's a transvestite, I thought, as I picked up his book of stamps and got out of the car. There was no answer to my knock on the door; they were probably in bed.

As this thought hit me I hurriedly pushed the stamps through the letterbox and walked quickly back to the car. Disturbing them in bed would have been too embarrassing.

Once back on the main road I heaved a sigh of relief, and tried to recapture the mood of twenty minutes ago, but I couldn't. I felt lonely and mildly depressed. Maybe it was time Gerald and I had a holiday. I decided to suggest it when he came home.

"We can't really go on holiday just at the moment," Gerald said. "The next cow is due to calve soon, I daren't risk anything happening to her. Is that a new dress?"

"Do you like it?"

"Yes, it's very nice, though I'm not sure yellow is quite your colour."

"It's not yellow, it's primrose," I said, hoping this might make it more acceptable. He hadn't noticed my hair.

"Perhaps we could have a holiday after she's calved," I said.

"We'll see...though it's going to be difficult leaving the animals."

Why hadn't I thought of this? I hadn't got any further than casting my mind round for boarding kennels for the dogs. What did farmers in our position do? All the other farmers in the area had men working for them...or sons.

"Perhaps Ernie would do full time for a week," I said.

"I'll mention it next time I see him, but we can't go for a while, anyway...do you want a drink?" he said, getting a couple of glasses out of the sideboard.

He mixed me a strong gin and tonic, and under its relaxing influence my mild depression drifted away. The subject of holidays was dropped.

Two mornings later, Gormless was standing under the holly tree on her own. I panicked instantly...it was still early and Gerald hadn't left for the train.

"I think Gormless is starting," I called up the stairs.

"What's she doing?"

"I haven't been across the field, but she's standing under the holly tree."

"It doesn't say anything in the calving book about standing under holly trees."

"Can you come and look at her with me?"

"Well, quickly...but I mustn't miss the train."

We looked at Gormless and she looked at us, then she wandered away and began to graze.

"She's OK. I must go. Can you just do me a piece of toast?" he said.

It seemed that farming was turning me into a nervous wreck. When we got back into the kitchen I realised that I would much rather have a gin and tonic than the cup of tea Gerald had poured for me. Somebody once told me that waking up feeling like a gin and tonic was a sure sign of alcoholism.

Around ten o'clock, Gormless was back under the holly tree. As I watched, she lay down, then stretched out flat on her side and rolled, kicking her legs. In the normal course of events cows don't do this. I phoned Gerald.

"I've only just got here," he said. "Get the vet, then give me a ring and let me know what he says. I'll try and come home after lunch; she won't have had it by then."

"Don't do this to me Gerald...they're your cows; you promised you'd be here." I hated the whine in my voice.

"I told you, I'll get there as soon as I can...that's if

she really is calving...now ring the vet."

This time I got hold of the proper cow vet and he arrived in the yard twenty minutes later, in time to help me turn Hippo and her beloved Charger out of the calving pen and into a small field. We'd called him Charger because he was so full of energy that he charged everywhere at full speed, with his tail stuck in the air.

Charger couldn't believe all the extra space he had suddenly been given and set off at a gallop, with Hippo lumbering along behind, mooing jerkily at him to come back.

We drove Gormless away from the fascination of the holly tree, and down the track, into the pen and straight into the corner, trapping her behind my makeshift crush. I had already filled the bucket with warm water and collected soap, and was beginning to feel a bit more professional about the whole business. It was very comforting to have the right vet there this time.

He examined Gormless and withdrew his arm with the news that the calf was presented the wrong way round, hind feet first, and he was going to have to get it out quickly. He went back to his car and returned with ropes and a block and tackle, which he proceeded to anchor to one of the support pillars of the barn. I felt sick. Even if Gerald was already on his way home he was going to be too late. I wanted him to be there so that he could see just what he was putting these poor animals through, then maybe he would reconsider farming, and we could get back to some kind of normal life.

We had tied Gormless to the rails, and I now pushed the gate against her as the vet attached calving ropes to the calf's hind feet inside her; then, as Gormless strained, he pulled with all his strength on the ropes. I spoke soothingly to her and rubbed her back, wondering whether this helped with cows as well as humans.

The feet and legs appeared, but the hips stuck.

"It's no good, I can't budge it. We'll have to use the block and tackle," he said and, attaching the calving ropes to a longer rope, he began winching the calf out, an inch at a time, while Gormless groaned. It can't have been much fun for the calf either. Visions of medieval torture racks filled my mind. Rotating the hips slightly he freed them and, with a few more pushes from Gormless, the calf was suddenly delivered. It sneezed.

"It's alive," I said, blinking back a few tears.

"Quick, give me a hand," he said.

Between us we dragged the calf to the side of the pen and hung it over the rails, head down to drain the fluid from its lungs. I stood there, trying to support the heavy slippery body as it struggled for breath. Then it started gasping occasionally, but didn't appear to be breathing in between the gasps. The vet had gone back to Gormless and was checking inside her. I called him.

"I think it's stopped breathing," I said, and started massaging its ribs.

He looked, then came quickly across and we lifted it off the gate. It slid onto the straw, a crumpled heap, eyes wide open in a fixed stare.

"It's dead!" I wailed. "It's bloody dead, isn't it?"

He rushed to his car and filled a syringe with something which he injected under the calf's tongue. It didn't work.

"I'm sorry," he said.

"I don't believe this," was all I could manage. I was

shaking inside.

"Can you give me a hand to get it out of the pen before she realises?" he said.

I helped him carry the future of the Warren Hanger herd, another fine bull calf, out of the pen, and round to the wheelbarrow.

"At this rate we're going to have to give over one field for a graveyard," I said bitterly. The vet apologised again.

"It's these exotic breeds; they have such enormous calves, there always seem to be difficulties with them. Some South Devon breeders elect for caesareans as a matter of course."

"Now you tell me," I said.

"I'm sorry," he said again. "Look, I know Harry Soutar had a couple of calves born yesterday. Would you like me to ring him and get you one for the milk?"

How come Harry Soutar managed to get calves born alive while we couldn't... probably because he, very sensibly, didn't have an exotic breed, I thought.

I couldn't leave Gormless without a baby, so I allowed the vet to get on with the adoption procedure and in quarter of an hour Gormless was the proud mother of a scraggy black and white bull calf, who eventually became known as Scruffy.

The vet left and I went back to the house. As I shut the back door, the phone rang.

"It's me. I've been trying to get hold of you for ages. Where have you been? What's happening?" said Gerald.

I burst into tears.

"Jill...what's the matter? What's happened? Jill, answer me...please. Stop crying, what's the matter?"

"It's dead," I spluttered.

211

"What's dead? What are you talking about?"

"It's dead. The calf. It was alive and then it was dead."

"Which calf?...Jill...which calf?"

"Gormless's," I made a supreme effort and got my hysterical gasps under control, before telling him the story.

There was absolute silence from the other end of the phone. Somebody spoke in the distance.

"Not now, Hazel," Gerald snapped. Then: "Is this some kind of a sick joke, Jill?"

"I wish it was."

"I'm coming straight home," he said.

"If you like, but there's really no point."

I opened the door into the garden so that the dogs could go out; there was a squirrel on the lawn, and he only just made it to the apple tree ahead of them. He shot right to the top, then turned round and swore at them, long tail twitching with rage.

The dogs went into total hysterics, Flicka even managed to climb the tree up to the first low fork, but was knocked off when Huggy joined her. I left them to enjoy their insane screaming for a few minutes, but the squirrel suddenly decided he'd had enough, and managed a nearly impossible leap to the wall at the bottom of the garden, and shot across the field to the oak tree. The noise subsided and the dogs embarked on a panting hunt for shrews in the long grass around the foot of the apple tree.

I made a cup of coffee. It tasted insipid so I added some brandy, which had a pleasant calming effect. The second one worked even better, probably due to the fact that I hadn't had any breakfast. A great lethargy descended over me like a warm blanket. There wasn't any desperate need for me to be doing anything, so I decided to give up on the day. Gerald was on his way home, he could look after the rest of the animals. A third and fourth brandy, taken neat because I hadn't the energy to make coffee, slid down very comfortably.

By the time Gerald arrived I was sound asleep, face down on the sofa with Huggy curled up on my back, and the empty brandy bottle on its side on the carpet.

I became conscious of a hand shaking my shoulder.

"Wake up - are you all right?" said Gerald.

"Go 'way," I mumbled. Huggy growled.

"Wake up," he said louder, shaking me again. "What's the matter with you?" Huggy bit his hand.

"You little bastard!" he shouted, punching Huggy off my back. Hug screamed and ran into the kitchen, and Rudi and Flicka began to bark.

I rolled over and sat up.

"What time is it?...and what have you done to my dog?"

"Little bastard bit me," he said, displaying a creditable set of teeth marks in his hand.

"Serves you right. Haven't you heard you are supposed to let sleeping dogs lie...and that goes for sleeping wives too."

My head was thumping and I staggered into the kitchen for an aspirin. Huggy cringed in his bed as I passed him.

"It's all right, Daddy didn't mean it," I told him.

"I bloody did," said Gerald, following me. "Why did the calf die?"

"I don't know; something about it coming out backwards and taking too long to be born. I can't remember, my head hurts, ring the vet and ask him. He said these huge cows are notoriously difficult calvers...

he asked for her calving history. Can we get rid of them?"

Gerald ignored this request.

"I can't believe we've lost both those calves. They were going to be the nucleus of our herd. Was it another big bull calf?" I nodded. "They'd have been sure winners in the show ring." His face began to crumple.

"You're not going to cry, are you?" My head didn't feel as if it could cope with a full-grown man in tears.

"Of course not. One of us falling apart is quite enough for one day." He pulled himself together with an effort. "Do I have to get another calf from Soutar?" he asked.

"I've already done it."

"I hope you got two while you were at it."

"It didn't occur to me. Look, can we please give up this idea of breeding cows? We don't know what we're doing and it's not fair to the animals. If you could have seen what he did to get that calf out, you..." He interrupted me.

"Well, that's it for the moment, then. As Hazel said after the other one, there are bound to be some upsets in the beginning. We've learned a lot in the last few months," he said soothingly.

"What's Hazel got to do with it?...All I've learned is that for us to try to be farmers is a really stupid idea." I tipped two aspirins into the palm of my hand, then added another for good measure.

"You're only supposed to take two of those," said Gerald.

"Why don't you go and do something useful like bury the dead calf – I'm going to bed."

"It's only three o'clock."

"My head hurts."

Gerald brought me up a cup of tea at half past six. I felt rough but lying there wasn't going to make me feel any better. The tea and two more aspirins restored me somewhat, and I spent the evening trying to persuade Gerald to give up on the cow breeding, but he refused to listen.

"We've had more than our share of bad luck now," he said. "You'll see, things will go right from now on."

CHAPTER TWENTY FOUR

We both avoided the subject of calving for the next few days, and Gerald was cheered up by an invitation from Jim, at the pub, to play for the village cricket team; their fast bowler had pulled a muscle in his shoulder, and the forthcoming match was to be a bit of a blood feud against the Rector's Eleven.

There was nothing very Christian about the team which the Reverend Tabe got together the following Sunday. It included three County cricketers and two Cambridge Blues from his university days, and none of them knew anything about turning the other cheek.

Gerald put up a surprisingly creditable performance, taking two wickets, which was pretty amazing considering the fact that he hadn't played since I had known him. But the Rector's side were all out to kill; and they did, in time for evensong.

I kept a low profile during the game; never a great fan of cricket, I didn't want to find myself roped in to help prepare cricket teas for future matches; but I had relaxed and was really enjoying the 'sorrow drowning' session in the pub afterwards; when the bar door opened, and Conor came in, holding the door open for the dark-haired woman I had seen him with in Chichester.

She was laughing up at him at a shared joke and his answering smile had real warmth. They crossed the bar to the dining area and she sat at a table for two in the corner, while he went to the bar for drinks and a menu.

Gerald was replaying the taking of one of his

wickets to an admiring audience, and I saw Conor's eyes flick over him with an enigmatic expression which I couldn't translate. He looked for me, then half smiled and nodded, before picking up his drinks and moving back to his companion.

Male eyes around the bar had followed her to the table, and who could blame them. She was very hard to fault; a perfect figure, given just the right accentuation by a well fitting scarlet dress, topped by that mane of black hair. Conversation had slowed slightly as she had walked in; allowing George and Ernie's voices to rise momentarily above the buzz. They seemed to be having an argument over the game of cribbage in which they'd been engrossed.

As Conor sat down the sound of conversation rose again, filling the busy bar, until above this sound came the scrape of George's chair being violently pushed back on the stone-flagged floor, and his raised voice shouting: "Well, bugger you!"

"And bugger you twice!" yelled Ernie.

"You come outside and say that!" George was red in the face.

"I bloody will." Ernie's chair fell over as he got up and he left it where it lay and stormed over to the door which George, with misplaced gallantry, was holding open for him. The two of them, both in their mid-seventies, disappeared round the back of the pub.

"Should somebody keep an eye on them?" I asked Jim behind the bar, trying to remember what the First Aid for a heart attack was.

"No, happens quite often. They'll swing a few punches which will miss because they've both removed their glasses, then they'll forget what they were arguing about and come back in as if nothing had happened."

I tried to ignore Conor and the woman, and was glad when George and Ernie created another diversion by coming back in, seemingly the best of friends, and started another argument as each tried to buy the other a drink. Gerald settled this one by buying pints for both of them, and they went back to their cribbage game.

Though dusk was falling, it was still light when we rattled over the cattle grid and started down the hill to the farm, disturbing a tawny owl who was perched on the telegraph pole beside the drive. It swooped silently away over the sheep and lifted up into the oak tree in the corner of their field. The sheep were grazing quietly, except for Quasi and Modo who were racing each other round the flock.

As I took my eyes off the two lambs, I noticed the elderly ewe which Gerald had brought from Oxford. She was walking round in a 'doddery' circle. Then she began to dance, but tripped on some rough ground and fell on her side. After kicking for a second or two, she went limp.

I stepped on the brake and Gerald lurched forward in his seat and put a hand on the dashboard.

"What's the matter?" he said, then he saw where I was looking.

"I think that old ewe just had a heart attack. She looks dead."

We got out of the car, and as we walked over to her, dodging the twins on the way, she got up, shook herself, and wandered back to the rest of the flock.

"She looks all right to me," he said.

"There's something wrong with her...she was dancing...in a circle."

He gave me a funny look

"Dancing...I see. I thought I was the one who'd been drinking."

"No, really, Gerald, she was."

"Well, she looks OK now."

The old sheep was grazing quietly with the others, and Quasi and Modo had dived under Nasty for their supper. They were getting quite big and the enthusiastic butting at her udder, in their attempts to get her to let down some milk, were almost lifting her off her feet.

We watched the old ewe for a few more minutes, but she did nothing unusual, so we drove on into the yard.

As we got ready for bed Gerald said: "Bit of all right, the woman that Conor bloke brought in. Don't really go for black hair myself but I wouldn't push that out of bed."

"Thanks!" I said. The unsettling thought that Conor and she were probably also on their way to bed slipped into my mind.

"No, sorry...I didn't mean it like that," Gerald added hurriedly .

"So how did you mean it then?" I was angry for reasons that even I didn't really understand.

"Oh, you know...it's just one of those silly things one says."

"Well, don't," I snapped, getting into bed and picking up a book.

Gerald got in beside me and put his arm round me.

"Sorry, darling," he said soothingly, nuzzling the side of my neck.

"No," I said.

"What d'you mean...No?"

"I mean, no; you are not going to make love to me while you're thinking about black haired women in scarlet dresses. Go to sleep."

"I'm not thinking about black haired women in
219

scarlet dresses, you silly moo."

"Calling me a 'silly moo' isn't helpful either."

"Oh, for God's sake." He flung himself over with his back to me, and in a minute he was sound asleep, and snoring the comfortable snore of one lubricated with several pints.

I lay awake for ages, until I remembered an old trick a friend used for inducing sleep. If I'm still awake in ten minutes, I thought, I'll go down and clean the oven.

I was dragged out of a deep sleep and a weird dream about driving a fire engine through a flock of dancing sheep. The alarm clock said one a.m. and I could still hear the bell of the fire engine. I got out of bed. Gerald stirred and muttered something.

Opening the window, I realised the noise was coming from the Barrington-Smythes' empty cottage.

"It's their bloody burglar alarm," Gerald said, coming fully awake.

I closed the window.

"Do you think we ought to phone the police?"

"No - let them get bloody burgled," he said.

I got back into bed. The alarm rang on.

"Do you think that thing is connected to the police station?" I said. I was a bit hazy about how burglar alarms worked. We didn't really need one with the three dogs.

"Probably," said Gerald, dozily.

How could he drift off to sleep with that noise going on? He couldn't. He tossed and turned and cursed, and eventually told me to go and phone the police and get them to turn it off.

I was halfway down the stairs before I wondered why I was doing this, then decided that 'middle of the night calls to the police' must obviously classify as 'women's work'.

The police were very helpful, and said they would ask one of their patrol cars to call in... Twenty minutes later two patrol cars, sirens going and blue lights flashing, gave the valley owls something to think about. If there had been a burglar, he would have been miles away with his loot by now.

I watched from the bedroom window as torches flashed and flickered round the empty cottage and over the alarm box fixed to the wall, just below the roof. The alarm continued to ring.

A policeman came to the farm and asked if we had a key to the cottage. He said there didn't appear to have been a break-in; it would seem that something had tripped the alarm.

"Very delicate, some of them are," he said.

I told him we didn't have a key, and he said, in that case they would have to contact the firm who manufactured the alarm and get them to turn it off sometime tomorrow.

"Why haven't they stopped it?" asked Gerald, as I returned to bed.

"They can't, not without getting into the house. It can't be turned off until tomorrow."

"What?" shouted Gerald. "How am I supposed to get to sleep through that racket?"

"How are *we* supposed to sleep through that racket?" I corrected.

We lay there...Gerald swearing every two minutes and flinging the covers about, while I tried various ploys like: fingers in ears, head under pillow, and eventually cotton wool ear plugs. But the clatter of the alarm was totally invasive and scornful of my feeble efforts to gain silence.

Suddenly Gerald flung back the covers and leapt out of bed.

"Where are you going?" I asked.

"I've got the answer. You go back to sleep."

"Back to sleep!" further words failed me.

Gerald banged and crashed about downstairs, upsetting the dogs, then returned to the bedroom and flung open the window. I saw what he was carrying.

"No, Gerald. You can't."

"I bloody can. Just bloody watch me," he said.

He loaded a cartridge into the 4.10, took careful aim at the burglar alarm, and shot out one of the Barrington-Smythes bedroom windows.

"Oh!" he said.

I got an hysterical fit of giggles.

"It's not bloody funny," he said, but I couldn't stop.

"Why don't you do something useful, like make a cup of tea?" he said.

I stumbled off downstairs, still snorting and trying to control myself. He joined me in the kitchen.

"How are you going to get out of that, then?" I asked, with a slight break in my voice, and my back to him.

"They won't know it was us," he said.

"You - not us," I corrected. "And of course they will. There will be shotgun pellets all over the bedroom." I stifled another giggle.

"If anyone asks, I'll say there was someone out early shooting rooks, but I didn't see who it was," he said.

"Is this the right time of year for rook shooting?"

"Well, pigeons then," he replied, looking for somewhere to hide the gun and cartridges.

"Here, can you find somewhere to lose these?" He

222

thrust them at me.

"I'm not getting my fingerprints all over them; you do your own dirty work."

"I'll put them up in the roof," he said and, fetching the stepladder, he spent the next five minutes banging about in the roof over the landing, cursing builders who did not install electric lights in roof space as standard practice.

When the noise he was making finally ceased, I suddenly realised it was eerily quiet.

"Gerald. It's stopped."

"What?"

"Listen."

"I can't hear anything," he said.

"That's what I mean, idiot. It's stopped. You must have got it with a stray pellet."

"It was a stray pellet that got the window; the burglar alarm got a direct hit," he said.

"Oh, all right, let's get back to bed." I wasn't going to argue the toss at three o'clock in the morning.

The Barrington-Smythes were away in Hong Kong and it was her mother who arrived to let the alarm engineer in the following day. I watched him pointing out the trajectory of Gerald's shot to her, as they studied the broken window. By the time she had arrived on the doorstep, I had decided the only course of action was to admit the damage, put up a good case for why the alarm had driven us mad, and offer to pay for the repairs. Gerald, fortunately, was in London, or he might possibly have landed himself in prison for criminal damage and unlawful use of a firearm.

Luckily for us, the old lady had herself been kept awake most of the previous night by a car alarm which nobody had bothered to turn off, and the matter went no further.

CHAPTER TWENTY FIVE

Two weeks later I found the old ewe dancing again. As I walked the dogs down the drive, I watched her spinning in a circle; then she fell down facing the bank and hedge on the far side of the field. She didn't go right over, but lay with her chin resting on the bank.

I went over and knelt down beside her. She wasn't unconscious, but looked dazed and made no attempt to get up as I reached her. Rudi studied at her with his head on one side for a moment, then joined Huggy and Flicka who were following the scent of a rabbit along the field boundary.

I sat on the bank beside the old girl, waiting for her to recover, while the dogs searched the rabbit holes under the old hedge.

Brambles, carrying large juicy blackberries, trailed thickly through the prickly hawthorn. This was the north side of the hedge and the berries were twice as luscious as the fly-blown ones on the sunny side. I decided to come back later and pick some for a blackberry and apple pie to cheer Gerald up. It looked as though I was going to have to give him bad news about the ewe, and anyway the blackberries had to be picked soon because Margaret had told me that after the first of October the devil spits on them.

The ewe made a gurgling sound, but didn't move. I began to worry that her odd behaviour could be due to a brain tumour, and quickly became convinced that this was the case.

She had fallen awkwardly, and I pulled one of her

back legs into a more comfortable position. The dogs bolted a rabbit back across the field towards the house, and went after it in full cry. This disturbance prompted me into action, and I decided to shut them indoors and phone the vet.

The surgery said they would ring him on his mobile phone, as he was in the area, and he pulled up in the yard about a quarter of an hour later. It was the proper farm vet.

"Hear you've got a problem with a ewe."

"She's done this before," I told him. "But last time she got up and seemed all right. I'm worried that she might have a brain tumour."

"You say she was circling?"

Sitting sideways on the car seat, he changed his shoes for wellingtons as we spoke.

"Yes...and the other time as well."

"It does sound like it." He collected his bag from the boot of the car, and we set off across the field towards the ewe.

"How old is she?" he asked.

"I don't know...pretty old."

As we reached her he looked at her grey whiskers and searched for her non-existent teeth.

"Mmm...she is old." He looked into her pupils with a torch. "Mmm...I'm not sure."

"Do you think she is suffering...I mean might she have a ghastly headache...do sheep get headaches?"

"Well, it is coming up to 'tupping time'," he joked.

I was too worried to appreciate his humour, because it had just occurred to me that I was on the verge of making a life or death decision. I looked into the ewe's unfocussed eyes.

"I don't want her to suffer and then have to have

her put down later on, when she's pregnant. What do you think?"

"Well, it's up to you...it's either a brain tumour or epilepsy...either way she's not much good to you...and she is very old."

Taking a deep breath I made the decision.

"Right...put her to sleep then...before I change my mind, and then we have to do it later."

"Can you move those into another field?" He nodded towards the rest of the flock.

Between us we drove them down the track to the meadow by Conor's wood, and returned to the ewe, who still hadn't moved. The fact that she didn't seem to have noticed she was now alone convinced me we were doing the right thing.

The vet was carrying a bottle of anaesthetic and a syringe, which he'd collected from his car. It occurred to me that I hadn't asked Gerald if he agreed with what I was doing, but it was too late now.

"I thought you used a humane killer on farm animals," I said.

"Not if I can help it...it worries the rest of the stock." I was surprised by this thoughtfulness, after his rather cavalier attitude towards Cheap when he was sick. He filled the syringe.

"Can you hold her head up?" He searched for a vein in her neck, and pushed the needle in. She didn't move and gradually went limp. He put his stethoscope to her chest.

"Mmm...tough old bird...that lot should have done it." He refilled the syringe. It took the whole of the second syringe before he finally pronounced her dead. As he left, he gave me the phone number of the Hunt kennels.

"They'll pick her up tomorrow and dispose of her for you. Tell them to incinerate her, not feed her to the hounds, unless they want the pack anaesthetised... Can you get her inside somewhere for the night? Stop the magpies and foxes getting at her."

"My husband can move her with the tractor when he comes home."

"Right...better luck with the rest of them. 'Bye."

"Thanks. Goodbye."

As he went up the drive I looked across the field to the still white mound beside the hedge. It didn't seem decent to leave the ewe lying there exposed, so I fetched an old dog blanket and covered her over, watched by two magpies in an oak tree in the corner of the field. Their harsh chattering brought two more young ones flying in to join them. They gave the impression of vultures gathering, and suddenly I felt shaky. Conor's words came back to me –'where you have livestock, you have dead stock' - it seemed to me that we were having more than our share of dead stock... If you counted the chickens, there had been ten deaths on the farm since we came.

I phoned Gerald and told him what I had done. He was not pleased, saying that he had paid a lot of money for the ewe, on the strength of her pedigree, and he felt sure we could have got at least one lamb out of her before getting rid of her. This heartless attitude prompted me into a lie about the vet having said she was suffering. Information which he accepted with bad grace, but by the time he arrived home that evening he was resigned to her loss.

I helped him roll the body onto the tractor forks, gagging as I did so having found that the magpies had managed to pull back the blanket and remove her eyes.

This didn't seem to upset Gerald particularly. It seemed he was much more worried about the prospect of witnessing birth than death. He drove her down to the stable in the top yard, and as we dragged her into a dark corner, I explained that we had to tell the kennels about the anaesthetic when they came to fetch her.

Next morning I found him in the stable with the spray can of the purple antibiotic I had used on the navels of Nasty's lambs.

"What are you doing?" I asked.

"I don't want them feeding her to the hounds by mistake...they may have other dead sheep at the kennels, so I thought I'd do this."

He had started to write on the ewe's side with the spray and had already done I N C I but by the time he had finished the next N, he had run out of space. He put a dash, and said: "Help me turn her over."

I didn't want to. The ewe's body had swollen up during the night and the skin over her stomach was as tight as a drum. The smell was pretty bad, too. I backed out of the stable, trying not to breathe.

"Leave it, Gerald...we'll just tell them."

"I can't stop now...it won't make sense."

He pulled her over and sprayed - E R A T E - on her other side.

"Why didn't you just write BURN?" I said, trying not to laugh.

"Smart-ass," he said, as I staggered away, unable to stop the giggles.

He caught up with me as I went into the kitchen.

"I don't know how you can find this funny," he said. "I've just lost a lot of money there."

"I don't...it's a sort of defence mechanism I think...like when you shot the Barrington-Smythes.

228

How much did you pay for her?"

He looked at his watch.

"Heck...is that the time? I wanted to get in to the agricultural merchants; they close at twelve o'clock."

"You'd better hurry then...I'll see to the hunt."

It wasn't until after he had gone that I realised I still didn't know how much the ewe had cost...or anything else on the farm, apart from Cheap and Nasty. Perhaps I didn't want to.

Later, after the kennels trailer had left with its sorry and lethal burden, I decided to walk the dogs. The grin on the kennelman's face as he had pulled away up the drive was irritating me. He had read the ewe's flank as he winched her into the trailer.

"Was that her name ERATE? Is it Latin?"

I was a bit tired of having to justify some of the weirder things Gerald had done. He never seemed to be around when it came to apologies and explanations.

It was a brisk, windy day, with small cumulus clouds sailing across the sky. A good blow on the common with the dogs would brush away the slight bad temper which had settled on me, and hopefully get rid of the smell of decaying sheep which had lodged in my nostrils.

Keeping the dogs under control through the wood, I manoeuvered us through, and over the stile onto the common and bent to unclip their leads.

"Hear you've been shooting the neighbours." Conor had appeared silently behind me.

"I wish you wouldn't do that," I snapped, before I could stop myself...my heart slowly creeping back to its correct position.

"I'm sorry...did I startle you?"

"Yes...who told you we'd shot the neighbours?"

"Oh, I heard it up in the shop. Margaret thinks it's very amusing...the B-S's aren't all that popular."

"It was their burglar alarm. There was no one to turn it off. I think after two hours of its continuous ringing, you could safely say that Gerald and I were both of unsound mind when he took that drastic action."

He smiled, my knees weakened.

"Sorry about your sheep," he said.

"Does everyone know everything the moment it happens, around here?"

"Oh yes... and I'm afraid with you being newcomers you get more attention than most."

"How long does it take to stop being a newcomer?"

"I don't know...I've only been here a couple of years...don't worry though, they like you."

"Only because we make them laugh." I tried not to sound bitter.

"Don't worry about them. Must go." He grinned, raised a hand and climbed over the stile into the wood.

"I don't want to be a laughing stock," I told Huggy grimly, as I let him off the lead. He jumped off the sandy path into the heather, then stopped short. Just in front of him was a large adder. I stifled a shriek, in case it brought Conor back and gave the village another excuse for amusement. Fortunately Huggy was wary, and all the snake wanted to do was get away, but it made for an uncomfortable walk after that. You can't enjoy beautiful views when your eyes are glued to snake-infested paths.

Gerald arrived home with a smart leather 'tupping' harness for Henry, complete with red, blue and yellow marker crayons - to show which ewes he had covered.

"I saw a huge snake on the common," I told him. "Huggy nearly stepped on it."

"Pity he didn't...now let's see how Henry looks in this. I think I'll use the red marker."

"That's not very nice. Poor Hug. You're not going to put Henry in with the ewes yet are you? I thought you said October."

"Well, it's nearly October."

"Don't you have to 'crutch' them first?"

"Crutch what... what's that? It sounds rude."

"The ewes. That's what Erica called it. You have to shear away the wool round their naughty bits to make it easier for Henry."

"How do sheep manage in the wild?" he asked.

"I don't know...I've never thought about it."

"Well, then, can you do them for me tomorrow? You've had more experience, what with shearing Nasty."

"No, Gerald. If I could catch and hold them single-handed, it would take me about a year to do all of them. It took three hours to shear Nasty."

"Three hours! They do it in half a minute on those documentaries."

"You do it then...and find out how easy it is. I don't mind holding the ewes for you."

After my epic shearing of Nasty, Erica had brought over a pair of hand shears which, though they looked like something off the film set of 'Far from the Madding Crowd', were actually remarkably efficient. I got these out for Gerald, and after lunch we fetched the ewes into the barn.

We trapped the first one in a corner, and I held her still for him. He walked round to her back end, wrinkled up his nose and said, "Ugh! She's filthy."

"They all are."

"Have you got any rubber gloves?"

"Only the washing up ones. I'll get them."

He struggled to fit his large square hands into the yellow plastic gloves before muttering something about my 'stupid small hands', and flinging them onto the straw. I grabbed hold of another ewe.

"You said my small hands were going to be a great asset, come lambing time," I reminded him.

"Hold her still," he said and started trying to remove the disgusting matted wool from the sheep's back end.

"There's something wrong with these shears," he said. "You must have blunted them on that idiot ewe of yours."

"I did Nasty with scissors. Erica said it's a knack...you don't seem to have it." His current bad temper and unkind remark about Nasty had annoyed me...she had been very good since producing the twins.

"That's nothing to do with it, it's these bloody shears, they're useless. I'm not struggling with them any more. Turn the sheep out again."

"Hey, don't order me about like that. I'm not your farm hand."

"Sorry, darling, it's these stupid animals. Why do they have to get in such a mess?"

Ernie and I got the ewes in a few days later, and he 'crutched' them very efficiently with the hand shears. I helped him until, as I pushed a ewe over to him, he leered unnervingly at me.

"Yer good with the animals...yer woiry," and ran his eyes appreciatively over my figure...which, even with the wildest stretch of the imagination, could never be considered 'wiry'. I hurriedly put a couple of ewes between us and offered to go and make him a cup of coffee.

Gerald seemed to have gone off the sheep a bit and 'tupping' wasn't mentioned for a while, though he did hang Henry's new leather harness up in the kitchen, where he could admire it.

CHAPTER TWENTY SIX

On the first of October Gerald decided it was time to embark on our sheep-breeding programme. I was pegging out clothes on the line in a soft golden autumn sunshine when he came into the garden, swinging Henry's leather harness. As usual he took it for granted that I would drop whatever I was doing to help him.

"Right, what I want you to do is bring the ewes down to Henry's field after I have put the harness on him," he said.

Henry by this time was nearly as tame and friendly as Cheap, and would allow certain liberties to be taken with him, as long as he was rewarded with sheep nuts.

"Let me just finish this," I said, rescuing a sock which Rudi had stolen from the basket, and carried away across the garden to where he and Flicka were using it as a tug of war rope.

"Can't you control those dogs? That's one of my best socks. Come on, I want you to get the ewes."

"We should have accepted Ernie's offer of a sheep dog; it would have saved me a lot of running about," I complained.

"Not that bloody thing - it still glares at me out of the back of his pick-up. Lead them down with Cheap...it's easy," he said. "Where did you put the marker crayons?"

"You put them on the scullery shelf."

I collected Cheap's halter and waited by the garden gate. From there I would be able to see Gerald's signal that he was ready for the ewes. Then he came back up the steep track.

"I'm not sure about this harness thing," he puffed. "Can you just come down and check that I've got it on right?"

I returned to the field with him and found Henry looking rather puzzled.

"I can't move my legs,"he baa-ed.

"I don't think he is going to do much tupping like that," I laughed. "You seem to have got it on upside down...I'm sure that crayon thing shouldn't be on top of his back."

"I rather wondered about that," he said.

Between us we removed the harness and replaced it with the marker correctly positioned on Henry's chest, and I went to fetch the ewes.

Once haltered up, Cheap did his 'bellwether' impersonation and, with him trotting along beside me, we led the ewes through the top yard, past the house and down the hill. Gerald was stationed at the gate of Henry's field to let us all in.

With the girls following nicely grouped behind us, I was just congratulating myself and Cheap on the ease of the operation, when Gerald, out of tune with the animals as usual, opened the gate welcomingly wide while we were still halfway down the track.

Henry, who had been standing behind him, eyes riveted on all the approaching 'crumpet', tossed his head and charged through the gate at a gallop.

Raising dust as he hurtled towards us, he shot straight into the centre of his harem, who turned back, scattering in all directions with Henry tearing from one to the other sniffing and trying to mount them.

In his excitement he mounted Cheap as well. This indignity was too much for Cheap who turned round and pulled me into the fray, as he tried to drive Henry away from the ewes. I slipped, a ewe banged into the back of my knees and I went down, cursing Gerald, and dropping Cheap's rope as several of the ewes stumbled and jumped over me in a panic to preserve their virginity.

"Are you all right?" asked Gerald, pulling me to my feet.

"Don't ask bloody stupid questions. Why the hell didn't you wait till we reached the gate?" Blood was trickling from the back of my hand which had been sliced by a sharp pointed hoof.

"I didn't know Henry was going to come out, did I?" He sounded aggrieved.

"Well, you can get them back in yourself. I'm going to patch up my hand before it goes septic...I'll probably get lockjaw."

"How can I get them in on my own?" he called after me.

"Try a bucket of sheep nuts. Some of the greedier ewes might follow a bucket."

My hand was taking priority, and I knew the sheep couldn't actually get out onto the road. Should they get that far, they would be stopped by the cattle grid at the top of the drive.

From the window, as I wrapped a bandage round the injury, I could see Gerald running around the top yard, chasing odd bunches of sheep, in an attempt to get them back into one flock.

Henry and Cheap were having a major 'set to' outside the feed store, watched admiringly by Nasty and the twins. I suddenly realised that I should have separated Nasty and the twins from the flock; we didn't want any more half breeds. I hoped it wasn't too late.

The three older ewes had discovered the hay and were busy pulling at it through the netting. The back door banged.

"Jill, get out here and give me a hand. I can't cope with this lot single handed."

"I won't be a minute...I can't find a safety pin."

"Oh, for Christ's sake come on!" He went back outside, leaving the door open. Before I could reach it the three dogs had shot off after him, and were joining in the fun.

The postman's van drove slowly into the yard.

"It's like the Calgary Stampede out there," he grinned, handing me the mail.

I could have done without his appearance. 'Tupping Time at Warren Hanger Farm' would be all over the village by tomorrow. Gerald came momentarily into view round the end of the barn. He appeared to be beating Cheap with a shovel.

"Gerald - stop that!" I shouted, as I took the letters and tried to smile at the postman. He turned his van round carefully and set off up the drive.

I ran to the feed store and half-filled a bucket with sheep nuts. The three old ewes heard the rattle of the bucket and trotted towards me. Calling: "Sheep, sheep, sheep," I set off once more for Henry's field.

Nasty and the old ewes reached me first, and as we went down the track the flock grew in size; by the time I reached the gate they were all with me, including the over-excited Henry, mouth open, panting ferociously with his black tongue hanging out.

I ran through the gate and halfway across the field, before emptying the bucket on the grass, where the sheep all fell on the nuts, pushing and shoving against each other. I managed to get a rope round Nasty's neck and dragged her back out of the field. The twins followed.

"It's easy when you know how," I said triumphantly to Gerald.

"Well, they know you," he said.

I caught Cheap and persuaded him to leave the scattered sheep nuts with the promise of a whole pocketful to himself. Then I eased him out of the field and we led Nasty and the twins back up the hill to the field above the house. I liked having them there because I could watch the twins playing from the kitchen window.

As we got back into the yard, Ernie's pick-up pulled in.

"Thought I'd just pop in and see if you needed a hand with anything," he said.

He's met the postman, I thought.

"No, I don't think so, thanks," said Gerald. "We've just put the ewes in with Henry - he seems happy." He gave a conspiratorial man-to-man grin.

"Oh, right." The disappointment in Ernie's voice showed that he had met the postman, and now he'd missed all the fun. His eyes fell on my bandage.

"What's up with your hand?" he asked.

"A sheep stood on it," I said.

Before I could elaborate, Gerald stepped in.

"Would you just come and have a look at the tractor a moment?" he asked Ernie, and they walked away towards the tractor shed, talking machinery.

By the next morning four ewes in Henry's field had large red blobs on their back ends, Henry had calmed down a bit, and Gerald was already talking about how successful the resulting lambs would be in the show ring.

CHAPTER TWENTY SEVEN

Both the original Primroses had been tested, and found to be in calf. But because these were by an Aberdeen Angus bull, and would be half breeds, Gerald wasn't particularly interested in them; nor was he interested in the two 'bought in' calves, Charger and Scruffy. They were a constant reminder of the two who had died, and it wasn't long before he found a neighbouring farmer who agreed to buy them to rear on for beef.

As I weaned them ready to go, the farm echoed to the bawling of the calves shut in the calving pen, and the miserable bellowing of their foster mothers out in the field.

But after a week I had taught the calves to drink their powdered milk mixture out of a bucket, and the cows' milk was drying up nicely: and I had had enough of the noise - and Gerald's complaints about the noise - and was glad to see the calves go.

I said as much to Ernie as we were looking at the two pregnant Primroses, over the gate one morning.

"I allus said no good would come of them," he said. "Yer not s'posed to rear them cattle north of Dartmoor. That's why they calls them South Devons," he accentuated the South. "If 'e wanted cows that colour why didn't 'e get Sussex?"

"I didn't know there were Sussex cattle." As usual, Ernie was standing much too close to me. He didn't stand this close to Gerald; did Ernie really think I might find him attractive? I looked at the wrinkled turtle-neck protruding from the frayed collar of a grubby shirt, then up to his face as I backed away slightly. A sharp, lined face with two deep grooves each side of his nose, two days' grey stubble, and no teeth. He never wore his teeth to work. I made a mental note to check whether he wore them to the pub.

He went on: "Yes...I'd a thought 'e'd have liked them Sussex cattle; they're rare, and a better colour than them things," he nodded towards the Primroses.

"Rare? Don't tell him about them, Ernie, please," I begged. "I'm sick of cows."

"They rats'll be coming back soon. 'Ave you got some poison? Mind you, you'd better just check for a few evenings. I did 'ave a pair of barn owls down in the bottom barn last year; 'aven't seen them for a while now though. You don't want to poison them. They'll kill the rats for you. Roight, I'll be off then. See you next Wednesday."

He walked away up the hill, leaving me leaning on the gate, looking down towards the bottom barn, visualising two grey shapes swooping silently in through the wide, high door, and up onto the oak beams that supported the sagging, moss-covered, tiled roof.

From my position halfway up the hill, I could see over the top of the barn, and away down the valley, which stretched for about four miles. Steep hills rose on either side, covered by plantations of coppiced chestnut, and ancient broad-leaved woodland. Springs rising in these hills became streams, which flowed down to join the brook winding its way through the valley bottom. In the distance the South Downs rose, sheltering the valley from the worst of the prevailing west wind.

From my viewpoint I could see no houses or roads; they were there I knew, but hidden by the trees. The scene looked wild and reminded me of parts of Exmoor. I had a sudden idea for a short story.

Racing back to the house I found a large pad and a biro; three hours later I was reading it through over a cup of coffee, and it was good, a love story set on Exmoor, involving smuggling and a slip back in time for a twentieth century couple.

I showed it proudly to Gerald when he came home.

"There!" I said... "Daphne du Maurier, or what?"

He finished reading it and looked up with a grin.

"More like Daphne Woodbine. I don't think that's quite Booker Prize material."

The comparison of expensive du Maurier cigarettes with Woodbines, the cheapest brand of that era, was hurtful, even if it was quite funny. I resolved never to write again...or if I did, never to show it to Gerald.

"Anyway, why are you using a biro, when I bought you that lovely word processor? Don't you like it?"

"I didn't have time to put it together, and I need to practise on it...I will soon."

I decided to set it up the next day and maybe try to write some letters on it.

In two weeks, very slowly, and with the aid of the instruction book, I was managing to get my new toy to process some words for me, and was thrilled at my achievement. But the muse had deserted me and disillusionment set in; maybe I wasn't destined to be a writer.

Now that the two multi-coloured calves had gone, Gerald cheered up a little about the cows. And after a talk with Harry Soutar, whom he met at the agricultural merchants, he began talking about embryo implants for Hippo and Gormless. Apparently they were the latest thing, needing complicated, expensive veterinary involvement.

I thought the cows had been through quite enough already and launched into a tirade about interfering with nature, cruelty to dumb animals and the dangers of genetic manipulation. Gerald sat quietly through this until I stopped to draw breath.

"If they'd had genetic engineering when you were born," he said, "they'd have been able to engineer you without a mouth." Which of course made me laugh, but I think some of what I had said sank in, because he didn't raise the subject again, and when both cows bulled together a week later, it was the A.I. man who came to service them. It was Ernie's day on so the operation, using the cattle crush, went smoothly.

By now we were heading towards winter, and the weather was getting colder, the grass had gone and I was having to carry food for the animals again. During the summer, Gerald and Ernie had converted the bottom barn so that we could winter the cows indoors, to save them from turning the farm into a quagmire. Gerald had devised a system of linked garden hoses for delivering water to their trough in the barn, but had overlooked the fact that the hoses might need insulating. Something I discovered the morning after the first really hard frost.

After one look at the white, frost-covered fields from the bedroom window, I had indulged in house-wifely displacement activity for an hour, hoping the sun might come out; until guilt at the plight of our starving animals outside had finally forced me into my wellies. The sun wasn't going to come out anyway, the wind had got up, bringing in clouds and sleety rain from the east.

Leaving the house I walked fast down the hill to the bottom yard; going down wasn't so bad because the wind was at my back. The three dogs came with me, heads down, shoulders hunched and tails firmly tucked into their bottoms; they didn't cheer up until we reached the barn where they dived into the straw. First they had a good roll about, to get rid of the rain on their coats, then they set about a mouse-hunt in earnest.

As we had approached the barn where the cows were housed, it had registered that they seemed to be making an unusual amount of noise, considering there were only four of them. They all seemed to be talking at once.

A deep breath, to brace myself for the effort of carrying two heavy bales of hay in to them, proved a mistake. The cold damp air, laden with ammonia from gallons of overnight cow pee, induced a painful fit of coughing.

I discovered that the cows were bellowing because they had been deprived of water by the exposed hoses, which had frozen solid during the night, and in protest the thirsty beasts had overturned and wrecked their empty water trough.

As I studied this problem, a dull thud and a startled 'baa' from behind the barn told me that Nasty was out and had broken into the stack yard, where she was pulling down the carefully piled bales of hay we hadn't had room for in the barn.

The cows were obviously in a very nasty mood, so I decided to deal with them first, by letting them out into the nearest field for a drink, while I sorted out the water problem.

The crushed trough was blocking the gateway into their pen, and the only way that I could get in to move it was to climb over the wall and attempt a death-defying trip through the discontented, milling herd.

I scrambled up, grazing my shin and hating the

person who had invented rough breeze-blocks. Sitting astride the wall, waiting for a gap to appear in several tons of angry pot roast, I remembered I had not had my signature witnessed on my new Will.

Gormless stopped to look at the crushed water trough, hoping probably that some kind of miracle had refilled it, and caused a major pile-up behind her. Seizing my chance, I dropped off the wall into a foot of cow muck, and ran for the gate. Pulling the damaged water trough out of the way, I unchained the gate and released a stampede through the yard towards the field. Apart from the fact that they were very thirsty, they had been shut in for a week now, and were not happy about it.

They galloped through the field gate four abreast. It was a 'three abreast' gateway and the gatepost cracked alarmingly as they forced their way through. I watched for a minute in the muddy gateway to see if any of them seemed injured.

They lumbered across the field to the stream, kicking their heels out sideways and making silly grunting noises, before sliding down the bank, dropping their heads and sucking in great draughts of water. Cows seem to need prodigious amounts of water.

When they had drunk their fill they went off on another skittish tour of the field, with Hippo taking exception to a high part of the bank under the hawthorn hedge. She kept charging it, rubbing up clods of earth and grass with her head and tossing them into the hedge. A Primrose thought this looked rather fun and went to join her.

Collecting the sledge hammer, I returned to the barn to try to sort out the dents in the water trough; a job I would rather have left for Ernie, but he wasn't due for a couple of days and the cows needed to come in again for the night.

Huggy had caught a mouse which he was burying in the earthen floor, just inside the barn entrance. He had scraped a small hollow, laid his kill in it, and was pushing earth and straw back over it with his nose. It looked like a very painful operation.

I turned off the water and disconnected the trough. After nearly an hour of swinging a seven-pound sledge hammer at the dents, I had managed to knock it into a shape which would almost stand level.

The morning was fast disappearing. I took hay out to the sheep and a bucket of nuts. Nasty, hearing the rattle of a bucket, appeared from the stack yard and followed me back to the field, to an ecstatic greeting from Quasi and Modo.

I re-stacked the bales she had knocked down and pulled the tarpaulin back over them, as my back began to ache. The next few jobs would have to be light ones; my muscles were not as young as they used to be.

Huggy was still guarding his mouse and I had to put a lead on him to take him home; the other two came fairly willingly as it was their lunchtime. We plodded back up the hill, against the wind and rain this time, lured on by the promise of a warm Aga, lunch and a coffee. I hadn't even managed to get my coat off in the scullery when there was a knock on the door.

It was a man from the Ministry of Agriculture who had come to count the cows for our suckler cow premium. Gerald had forgotten to tell me he was coming, but had apparently told him the cows would be in the barn. He wasn't very pleased when I explained that they were out in the field; and said he hadn't brought his wellies. We set off back down the hill and through the bottom yard.

The cows' field was empty. Through a new gap in the hedge, above the bank Hippo had been attacking, they could just be seen on the far side of the next muddy field. They had flattened the hedge making an escape hole about four feet wide. I called to them, but all they did was stare at us and he decided to count them from where we stood at the gate. They, in return, counted him - but seemed unable to agree on the total.

I invited him in for a coffee, and by the time he had told me all about his job, his holiday and his family, it was time to begin thinking about getting the cows in again, and doing the afternoon feeds before it got dark. It was still raining and the dogs showed no interest in coming with me as I set out for the bottom yard again.

The cows, tired of the freezing rain and being counted by Ministry men, had returned to the gate and were demanding their tea. They sounded like Gatwick airport at the height of the holiday season.

Before they could come in, though, their pen needed attention. I couldn't expect them to sleep in all that filth.

Collecting a wheelbarrow and a fork I started removing the dirty straw. The full barrow then had to be manhandled through the mud, and round the barn to the dung heap at the back. As I pushed it up to the top of the heap, on the ramp made from the old chicken run door, which was now wet and slippery, the barrow slid sideways and emptied itself onto the ground, pulling me to my knees in the stinking mud as I struggled to keep it upright. One advantage of isolation is that you can use really terrible swearwords very loudly. I took out two more barrows before it began to get almost too dark to see, then gave up and put some fresh straw in the pen.

I filled the hayracks and re-connected the water trough, quite proud of my repair job. Then I went across the yard and opened the gate to the cows' field, standing well back from a repeat of the morning stampede.

Leaving them tucking into the hay, I carried another bale over to the sheep before trudging up the hill in the dark, the rumbling of my stomach reminding me that everyone had been fed except me. I wasn't counting the last of a packet of digestive biscuits I had shared with the Ministry man.

"Ooh...nice and cosy in here," Gerald said as he came home later, standing in front of the Aga, sniffing appreciatively at the lamb stew keeping warm in the bottom oven. "You don't know how lucky you are, Jill, it's horrible out there, and something had gone wrong with the heating on the train. It was freezing. I've a good mind to complain." He glanced at the clock. "Oh, look at the time...there's a programme I want to watch. Can you bring my dinner through on a tray?"

"Yes, your Lordship," I muttered. The story of my day paled into insignificance compared with faulty train heating, and would obviously have to wait until a more convenient moment.

There seemed to be a subtle gap opening up in our relationship, and I wasn't happy about it. I knew that he would deny there was anything wrong, and probably tell me I was imagining things if I mentioned it. I wished we could have a holiday, away from the farm and the bank, and try to get our marriage back to where it had been just before we left London. I resolved to try and put these feelings into some kind of sensible words at the weekend. Maybe I could also try again to get him to part with the cows. The sheep weren't so much of a handful.

CHAPTER TWENTY EIGHT

Having decided that Gerald and I needed to talk about our relationship, I found that I couldn't wait until the weekend, and broached the subject the following night, as we settled into bed.

"Gerald, are you happy?"

"What?"

"You seem a bit distant sometimes; are you happy here?"

"Of course - what do you mean, distant?"

"Well, I don't know. You seem a bit bored with me. I don't to get a 'goodbye' kiss any more...and do you know how long it is since we made love? Are you worried about anything?"

"For heavens sake Jill - I get tired - I travel and work all day and then there's the farm at the weekend. I'm not some kind of sex machine."

I didn't remind him that he used to be.

"I don't want you to be a sex machine, but we haven't made love for about three weeks...are you sure there's nothing wrong?"

"No, of course there isn't." He sighed..."All right," he said, putting on the lamp and pulling open the drawer of the bedside table, rummaging around for the packet of condoms he kept there. "We'll do it now, OK? Then perhaps I can get some sleep. I've got a busy day tomorrow."

"Not like this!"

"Not like what? Either you want to or you don't."

"I don't want to have to beg for it."

"I'm tired, Jill...and we're both too old to play this silly game. Go to sleep - I'll try to do better in the future." He switched off the bedside lamp, kissed me on the cheek, turned on his side and was asleep in a few minutes.

I lay awake looking up into the darkness, listening to his regular breathing. Perhaps I was wrong; after all, we were both in our middle years. If my first marriage had worked, maybe David and I would now be drifting comfortably along with lowered libidos, and expectations of each other.

Gerald was right, he did have a long day and a stressful job...was I expecting too much? Should I ask Erica how often they 'did it', for a comparison?

But it wasn't really the lack of sex that was worrying me - it was a general lack of warmth in our relationship. Something had changed and I couldn't work out what. Gerald submitted to hugs nowadays, rather than returning them.

I decided I was spending too much time alone on the farm. I should get out more, try to be more interesting. This was a nice thought, but when it came down to practicalities - by the time I had done the housework, fed and mucked out all the animals, come in, bathed, changed my clothes, put my hair into some kind of order and actually driven away from the farm, it was nearly time to come back, change, feed the animals and bed them down for the night, before cooking Gerald's supper.

"When do farmers' wives have time for a social life?" I asked Erica when she phoned for a chat next morning.

"They don't," she said, "apart from Harvest Supper and the Hunt Ball, not when they farm like you do.

Social life only becomes possible when you employ someone else to look after the farm. Can't you persuade Gerald to give up the cows, at least? Coping with those monsters is no job for a woman your age. He just doesn't understand. I suppose you could join the W.I."

"I can't imagine that making me more interesting to Gerald."

"Ho! Do I sense a problem?"

"No, not really; it's probably my fault. It's so difficult to look smart when staggering onto the dung heap with a barrow full of muck. Gerald was always pretty fastidious about his women."

"He's using you as cheap labour; you want to put your foot down."

"Probably, but I haven't forgotten how awful it was living on a knife-edge with David's temper. Gerald may be a bit selfish, well, unthinking really, but he's not dangerous, and it is lovely here. I wouldn't want to live anywhere else now. I'm in love with the farm and the valley and this corner of Sussex."

"Would you like to come to us for Christmas Day? We'd love to have you."

"That sounds great. I'll have a word with Gerald, but I'm sure he'll say yes. We went to his parents last year, but it was easier as we were in London. They won't want to come down here in mid-winter. Thank you, yes...an almost definite yes."

"What about Max?"

"No, he's spending Christmas with a new girl friend and her parents. They live in Hertfordshire."

"OK. Well, I'll speak to you before then anyway, Oh damn! Someone's just come into the yard, I think it's the feed rep. I'm sorry, I'll have to go and deal with him – Donald's out. Probably ring you later. Bye."

"Bye."

It was a blustery day, but not raining and I decided to take the dogs for a walk up onto the common before lunch, to fill up the time before Ernie left to go home. He was splitting logs in the top yard and kept finding excuses to come and talk to me. I took out a mug of coffee for him, and set off with the dogs.

A cloud of seagulls was wheeling and falling behind a tractor ploughing a stubble field further down the valley. As the tractor moved on they rose as one, circled the machine, then dropped again onto the newly turned earth behind the plough. I was momentarily surprised at seeing them in this countryside setting, until I calculated that they were only really about ten miles from the sea, south of the ridge of the Downs.

As we walked the footpath through the wood a white pheasant scuttled off the path into the undergrowth, but the dogs didn't take any notice. I could hear Conor's chain saw away to the right, and as I climbed the stile, could see him further up along the boundary fence, logging up last of the branches from the fallen oak.

The path on the common took us close to where he was working, and as he straightened up, he saw me and smiled.

"Do you need any logs?" he asked.

"Oh!...Yes, we will. Ernie left a few, but we've put in a wood-burning stove; we'll need some more."

"I'll bring you a load round when I've got this lot tidied up."

I thanked him and prepared to move on, but as he didn't seem to be in any hurry to return to his chain saw, I mentioned seeing the white pheasant in the wood.

"Yes, I've got two," he said. "There's a keeper up

on the Downs who breeds them specially. It helps me to see if mine are straying onto other peoples' land. We'll be shooting here soon, but I'll let you know which days, in case you have any nervous animals that might be worried by the guns."

"Thank you. Flicka doesn't like loud bangs."

"Is she all right after burying herself alive?" He bent down to where she was sniffing around his feet, and stroked his long elegant fingers smoothly along her dappled back, causing her to shiver with joy as his hand ran up her tail. I felt the frisson of every black and silver hair to the touch of his hand. It was time I moved on.

"Don't normally see you out here this time of day," Conor said, still seeming disposed to talk.

"No. I'm trying to avoid Ernie Challen; he's working in the top yard splitting logs for us, but he keeps finding excuses to talk to me...and he stands too close."

Conor smiled and stepped back a pace. I realised that he had been standing nearly as close as Ernie did, but I hadn't felt he was invading my space. Now I did suddenly feel uncomfortable. I remembered the black-haired woman, and said I had better get on. As I started to leave he spoke again.

"I've been meaning to thank you. Margaret told me it was you who dropped the stamps round. I'm sorry I wasn't in when you came."

"I was passing that way anyway. I love your cottage."

"So do I – I'm just negotiating to buy it from the Forestry Commission."

"Really?" My heart leapt; he was planning on living there permanently; then it sank, as I imagined him there with the black-haired woman with the sexy underwear.

"Well, best of luck...it's a magical place."

He had gone when we came back to the stile after circling the common. As the dogs and I crossed the field back to the farm after our walk, they suddenly dived into the hedge behind the chicken run. There was tremendous commotion and desperate squawking.

I beat them off and found that they had caught Slasher, goodness knows how he had got out. Clipping leads back onto their collars, I dragged them away, but Slasher didn't get up, he lay on his side with his legs thrashing. He looked mortally wounded. I waited a minute or two to see if he would die, but he didn't.

There was no way I could bring myself to wring his neck, and anyway I hadn't a clue how to go about it. Ernie would already have gone home. I would be laughed out of the county if I took Slasher to the vet to be put down. There was only one thing to do...I would have to shoot him.

Dragging the unwilling dogs back to the house, I got the 4.10 out of the cupboard and found the cartridges. Then I couldn't get the gun open to load it. This was the first time I had held a gun. After struggling with it for some minutes, I rang Gerald in London.

"The dogs have injured one of the chickens," I told him, "I'm going to have to put it out of its misery. How do I load the 4.10?" I wasn't going to tell him it was Slasher until he got home.

"Not again...how did they get in?..You're going to have to keep them under control; weren't you with them?"

"I couldn't help it, Sl...the chicken was outside the run."

"I don't think you ought to mess about with the gun. Wait till I come home, I'll see to it. Shouldn't you wring chickens' necks?"

"Gerald, it's in great pain...I have to do it now. I can't wring its neck."

Reluctantly he began to tell me what I had to do. Using my shoulder to cup the phone under my ear, I followed his instructions and loaded a cartridge into the gun as he spoke. Then, shutting the dogs in the kitchen, I went back out to the field. Slasher was still alive but obviously in great pain. Putting the muzzle of the gun against his head, I took a deep breath, said "Sorry", and pulled the trigger. Slasher was instantly dead, with a neat hole drilled just behind his ear.

As the gun banged, several of the hens rose into the air and flew across their run, and I realised that was how Slasher had got out...we had forgotten to re-clip the wings as their new feathers had grown back after they had moulted.

I toyed with the idea of preparing Slasher for the table, my mind visualising the steps necessary to achieve this operation, and very rapidly concluded that I couldn't do it. Though Slasher's one ambition had been to eviscerate a human, it was not something I could do to him. I buried him in our rapidly expanding graveyard in the field behind the bottom barn, and braced myself for another evening of defending the dogs against Gerald.

CHAPTER TWENTY NINE

Gerald, rather surprisingly, didn't say very much about the dogs' attempted murder of Slasher. I think he had been finding their battles rather less amusing since the bird had scored a deep furrow down his shin, leaving a dramatic white scar as it healed.

He arrived home with a large bunch of flowers, and was particularly nice to me all evening. Our talk of the previous night had obviously made an impression on him - either that, or the fact that I could now handle the 4.10. I relaxed, resolving to make more of an effort to present him with the wife he had married. It was going to be all right.

A few mornings later I actually caught Nasty escaping from her field. She was squeezing through the hawthorn hedge. As she wriggled her hindquarters free on the other side, the bushes snapped back behind her, leaving no hint of a gap. Quasi and Modo, dithered for a moment, then followed her through with a wiggle, and a buck and skip, as they chased after her down the track. All three made straight for the stack yard and the hay.

My heart sank. I didn't want anything to spoil the new, nice, tolerant Gerald who had just appeared, and I couldn't see him standing for three woolly Houdinis wrecking the farm. What we really needed was a sheep-proof fence round each field, but as none of his animals ever escaped, I couldn't justify the expense of this for my three mongrel sheep.

This looming problem was suddenly solved half an

hour later, as I waited in the shop for Margaret to finish serving the gentleman in front of me. He was telling her that he was going to get a couple of sheep to keep his orchard tidy; his little daughter adored sheep, so he thought he would get her some for Christmas.

In quarter of an hour the deal had been done, leaning on his car outside the shop. He agreed to take the whole family, Nasty and the twins, and arranged to pick them up on Christmas Eve.

Gerald was delighted, though he did say he would miss the lambs a bit, until I reminded him that, at the rate Henry was covering the ewes, he would have more than enough lambs to play with in the spring.

Things were beginning to go well at last. On Wednesday morning I helped Ernie to catch up the hens, and he clipped their wings. They seemed happier without Slasher bossing them around. Then I went indoors to make him a mug of coffee while he took some hay down to the sheep.

He came back looking very serious.

"You've lost another calf," he said.

"What! We haven't got any calves."

"It's one of them Angus calves. She's aborted. Dropped it in the corner of the barn...I've turned the others out. Probably best to get the vet to 'ave a look at 'er."

"Oh no! Just when I thought things were beginning to go right. Have you any idea why she lost it?" I was looking up the vet's phone number as I spoke.

"No, 'appens sometimes."

The vet didn't really know why either. Ernie helped me get Primrose into the crush for the vet to examine her, then wheeled the dead calf round to the graveyard behind the barn. A little brownish/black creature, it

256

seemed to have combined the coat colour of both parents.

The vet finished his examination of the cow, and said there didn't seem to be anything wrong which he could find...it was just one of those things. He gave her an injection and we turned her back into the barn. Ernie got the tractor out and buried the calf in the ever-spreading graveyard.

A mental count produced the gloomy statistic of twelve deaths on the farm since we moved in. I went back to the house, leaving Ernie to sort out the cows.

Just as I was deciding to delay telling Gerald about this latest disaster until he got home, he telephoned me.

"Jill, something's come up. There's a client I really must see tomorrow, but he's leaving for America in the morning, and the only time we can meet is around 7.30 am. so I've decided to stay up here tonight. Will you be all right on your own? Get Erica to come over or something."

"Of course I'll be all right on my own...the only time I've ever been scared here was the night you terrified me with the gun."

"Yes, I'm really sorry about that, it was a stupid thing to do. Is everything all right there?"

"No...I've just had to get the vet out to one of the Primroses. She's aborted her Angus calf."

"I don't believe it! What's the matter with Warren Hanger farm? I'm beginning to think the place is cursed. Is the cow all right?"

"Seems to be; the vet can't find anything wrong."

"That only leaves one cow in calf to show for nearly a year's work."

"I know. Please, could we seriously consider getting rid of the cows, Gerald? We're obviously not meant to have them."

"I can't think about that now, we'll have to talk about it tomorrow evening. Damn, what a bloody waste...Pardon?...Yes, Hazel, I'm just coming. I've got to go, Jill. Is Ernie there?"

"Yes."

"Well, get him to help you...I'll pay him overtime if you need to keep him on later today. See you tomorrow evening. Bye."

I had forgotten to ask Gerald where he was staying, in the unlikely event that I would need him. It didn't matter; if anything else did go wrong he couldn't do anything from London, and I could always phone Hazel if I needed to find out where he was staying.

Gerald had taken this last disaster much better than I had expected, and didn't seem inclined to blame me in any way for it. We seemed to be settling down into a more mature relationship. I began to relax and start thinking about Christmas, which was hurtling towards us.

Nasty's new owner arrived on Christmas Eve, with a trailer attached to the back of his Mercedes Estate. It seemed that the Nasty family was definitely moving up-market. I already had Nasty, the twins and Cheap shut into the stable in the top yard. Loading them was simple. I just led Cheap up the ramp, straight through the trailer with the others following, then he and I exited through the small door at the front end, shutting it in Nasty's face, while her new owner closed the rear ramp. I missed the three of them for days afterwards; somehow, with animals, you always become very attached to the naughty ones. They have entertainment value.

Christmas day was embarrassing. Not the trip to Erica and Donald's, but the rest of the day, before and after. I had heard of people being showered with gifts, but this was ridiculous...from the moment we woke on Christmas morning, Gerald began giving me beautifully wrapped gifts. He had spent hundreds of pounds, which we didn't have, on perfume, Kurt Geiger boots - two pairs, a leather jacket, a full-length suede coat, silk underwear to die for, silk pyjamas and dressing gown, a pearl choker necklace, emerald ring and bracelet, and other smaller items such as handmade chocolates. It made the waxed jacket I had given him look very meagre.

When I finished saying thank you - at about midnight - I finally got around to asking him why? "You're worth it," he said, which was really no answer at all. I thought perhaps he was feeling guilty about landing me with the job of farmer, and this was his way of trying to say sorry. I looked at all my presents laid out on the spare room bed that night, and realised there wasn't anything useful that I could wear around the farm. Even the underwear somehow wouldn't seem right under jeans and old jerseys.

On Boxing Day we went up into the village to watch the spectacle of the local hunt meeting on the green in front of the Royal Oak. To please Gerald, I wore my new leather jacket and one of the pairs of boots, only to have Ernie say, as we stepped out of the car: "See you're not planning to follow, then."

Everybody else was dressed in waxed jackets, flat caps, head-scarves and green wellingtons with little straps round the top, and nearly everyone on foot had a thumb stick. Terriers hurled abuse at passers-by through the windows of Land Rovers, and small children wandered in and out of the hounds, which stood in a well-behaved group around the master's huge bay horse, their sterns waving gently. They didn't seem to mind the many small, sticky hands patting them.

This good-humoured gathering was spoiled by a group of anti-hunt demonstrators who arrived in a battered old green van, and proceeded to wave banners and chant slogans. Their leader was about six feet tall, dressed in a black boiler suit, and had more metal rings threaded through the skin on his face than one would have thought possible. He must have really hated himself to have gone in for that degree of self-mutilation.

We went into the pub, and fought our way through the throng to the bar, to be greeted by Jim.

"Maybe they'll catch the blighter that took your chickens," he said.

"Oh, but they weren't...ooof," said Gerald, as I dug him in the ribs. "What was that for?" he asked.

"I let Margaret in the shop think it was the fox that killed the first lot of chickens," I whispered. "The village already thinks we're pretty incompetent as farmers without us giving them any help."

We went back out into the sunshine with our drinks, to watch the hunt move off. Half of the anti-hunt demonstrators had already set off across the fields, presumably in an attempt to cause chaos as the hounds drew through the first wood, searching for a fox.

"Let's go home and change, then we can follow for a while," I said.

"It's going to be awfully muddy, and you know I don't like walking far in wellingtons, they rub my legs. You go if you like, they seem to be heading in the general direction of the farm. I've got plenty I can do at home."

We went home, and I changed and set off across

our fields towards the faint sound of a horn in the distance. They seemed to be up on the common. By the time I reached the common, they had gone into the woods and were heading down towards the narrow road at the bottom of the valley. I took a short cut down to the road and waited, listening. Jays were screeching in the wood beside the road, but there were none of the parked Land Rovers which I had expected to find on the grass verge, as the less ambulant followed the hunt.

Then suddenly I could hear the sound of hounds in full cry, and they seemed to be coming towards me. I expected the sound of the horn and galloping hooves, but nothing else was stirring except what sounded like about thirty hounds coming fast through the wood, on the track which came out onto the road where I stood.

Then I could see somebody running, and as he came closer I realised it was the mutilated anti-hunt demonstrator. He had about eight puzzled-looking hounds trotting along behind him, and the sound of hounds in full cry, which I had heard, was coming from a portable tape recorder attached to the megaphone he was carrying. I could see a car coming in the distance, and quickly calculated that the hounds would arrive on the road at the precise moment the car passed by.

"Stop!" I shouted, as the megaphone carrier drew level with me. I moved forward to try to stop the hounds from running into the path of the car. He grabbed my arm and swung me round as the hounds milled about in the road. The car turned off before it reached us.

"Don't fucking interfere," he said menacingly, his horribly ringed face pushed close into mine.

Before I could say anything, he suddenly levitated about a foot in the air in front of me, and sailed into the ditch beside the wood. The tape recorder stopped, and in the silence the hounds heard the horn, sounding faintly, from deep inside the wood, and went loping off towards it through the undergrowth.

Conor stepped over to where the 'anti' was clawing his bedraggled way out of the ditch, and put his boot down on the tape recorder.

"Oops!" he said.

The 'anti' let loose a stream of foul language, and a detailed description of what was going to happen to Conor when the rest of the group found him. Conor ignored him and turned to me.

"Are you all right?"

"Yes, I thought the hounds were going to get hit by a car. Thank you for rescuing me. Look out!"

The anti had picked up a fallen branch and was raising it above Conor's head. He turned, ducked, and in a twinkling the 'anti' was back in the ditch.

"I'd stay there for a while pal, if I was you, and cool off. You keep this up and you're liable to get hurt." Conor turned to me. "Come on, the Land Rover's down here. I'll take you home; it's all getting a bit nasty here today."

As we got into the Land Rover, which was parked on another track just inside the wood, a police Range Rover passed along the road and stopped beside the bedraggled 'anti', who pointed towards us and showed them his tape recorder. They didn't even look in our direction as we drove off.

"Best not to say anything about this," Conor said. "The Press have nasty ways of making something out of nothing. You didn't see me throw that 'low life' into the ditch; the poor thing just slipped."

My answering giggle was slightly hysterical. Then

we were at the entrance to Warren Hanger, and I asked Conor to drop me at the top of the drive.

"Are you sure you're all right now?" His hand rested for a moment on my arm, and the intense blue eyes held mine for a second too long.

"Yes, yes, I'll be fine, and thank you again for rescuing me."

"I don't think you were in much danger...they're all cowards really, but it's not wise in today's climate, to go hunting alone. Take care." He watched me skirt the cattle grid, then made off with a wave.

I walked slowly down the drive, trying to stop my heart pounding, and telling myself it was only because of my confrontation with the 'anti'. I decided to do as Conor had said. I would say nothing to anyone - not even Gerald.

"Did you find them?" he asked as I went into the kitchen.

"No, I could only hear them. I think they went the other way."

"D'you want to go out this evening, or shall we feed the animals and put our feet up in front of the 'telly'?"

"That sounds cosy. My head's still feeling a bit fragile after that gorgeous red wine at Erica and Donald's yesterday."

It was an evening that I should have enjoyed, but I felt vaguely discontented, and I didn't want to have to keep feeling grateful for all the presents Gerald had given me. Rather than actually be grumpy with him, which he didn't deserve, I pleaded a headache and went to bed early, drifting off to sleep to the sound of a rising east wind as it began to whistle round the corner of the house.

CHAPTER THIRTY

As we went into January, the easterly winds gradually froze the ground into iron, making a perfect base for the snow which followed. It didn't take much snow or ice on our steep drive to make it impossible to get the cars up, and, rather than get trapped without transport, we took to leaving them at the top, and walking up and down. But even this could be hazardous when laden with heavy shopping.

There seemed to be a very short window of daylight in which to complete all the daily farm duties, and I found myself taking far more notice of nature's hints and warnings of future weather.

Dachshunds racing around with excitement was a sure sign of approaching snow, though when it actually arrived and froze their tummies, they were more than happy to 'crash-out' in front of the Aga, or the wood-burner in the sitting room. Even the cows would get a bit skittish when snow was on the way.

As the forecast was bad for the next few days, Gerald decided that a whole Saturday should be given over to a really good muck-out of the cows' winter quarters, and we turned them out into the field while he started the job with the tractor.

Our last pregnant Primrose was near to her calving time and beginning to show the physical signs we now knew we had to look for - a developing udder and the ligaments around her pelvic area slackening off. This loosening around the joints was making her walk as if she was coming unglued. The cows lumbered around for a minute or two enjoying the extra space, then started demanding hay. I tossed them half a bale and got on with feeding the sheep in the sunshine, enjoying the warmth of it on my back, but driven on to finishing the job quickly by the ominous bank of cloud which was slowly building up over the top of the hill.

The sheep were very hungry: hopefully all the ewes were pregnant, and they all seemed to be eating for three. Trying to get the sheep nuts poured into their trough before they mugged me was quite a hazardous operation, and nowadays I seemed to be permanently bruised around the feet and legs.

I went round to the stack yard and pulled down a bale of hay into the wheelbarrow - or hearse, depending on the job it was doing. Then, trying to push this gloomy thought out of the way, set off back up the track towards the sheep's field, the frozen ruts of the track jarring the barrow and making my wrists ache.

As I passed the cows, they reached over the fence to try and steal the bale. They had already nearly finished their hay, and what they hadn't eaten, they had trampled underfoot.

I swerved the barrow to avoid them, and suddenly noticed there were only three heavy heads straining over the fence towards the hay. My heart sinking, I looked up across the field to where the pregnant Primrose was lying - under the holly tree.

As I shouted for Gerald the sun was already disappearing, and the solid black bank of approaching cloud made a perfect backdrop for the holly tree, with its glossy dark green leaves and a heavy load of scarlet berries. At any other time I would have stood and appreciated this picture, but now, dropping the handles of the wheelbarrow, I ran back down the track. Gerald couldn't hear me over the noise of the tractor engine. I signalled to him to turn it off.

"What's the matter?" he said.

"She's started...she's under the holly tree." By now we were both convinced that any cow that got near the holly tree was about to give birth.

By the time we reached Primrose, she was rolling on her side and the calf's two front feet were already protruding. We were not going to get her down to the calving pen; at least she was getting some protection from the tree. The wind swirled the first few flakes of snow around us.

"Bloody stupid cow! In another ten minutes I'd have finished mucking out. You'd better go and ring Ernie, get him to come down. And fetch the calving ropes, they're in the scullery cupboard."

I rushed off, only too glad for once that I was not in charge and responsible for this calving. Ernie agreed, grudgingly, to come down. I was learning that Ernie's appearance of unwillingness was really an act. It meant that we always had to appear extra grateful for his help. It was not a hard game to play. I was sure Ernie secretly enjoyed coming down to us, as watching our attempts at farming provided him with endless material with which to regale his friends in the pub in the evenings.

Gerald waited beside Primrose as I put the other three cows back into their half-mucked-out pen, where they slipped about on the wet concrete floor and complained about their empty hayrack. Then I gave the sheep their hay, and by the time I got back to Gerald, Ernie was with him and a dark brown head had appeared to join the front legs. Primrose stood up and made an ungainly turn to inspect the spot on the ground where she thought the calf had arrived; it swung behind her as it slipped out to halfway down its ribs. Primrose arched her back and pushed, and her baby, now held only by its hips, shook its head and sneezed. Primrose thought she had finished and swung round again to inspect the ground. She pushed again and the calf was born. And that, I thought, is why cows are so stupid. They are all dropped on their heads at a very early age.

"I'll go and fetch the tractor to carry the calf," Gerald said, and set off across the field.

"Why do 'e want the tractor?" Ernie asked. "Calf'll be up and walking in a bit; you can drive them in." He looked up at the curtain of snow which was now approaching us, pulled up his coat collar and tipped his cap down over his forehead. "They look OK. I best be off before this lot really gets going."

I thanked him and he set off towards the bottom yard where he had left his van, waving to Gerald as the tractor trundled across the field towards me.

"Where's he gone?" Gerald asked.

"He said he wasn't needed any more. He was worried about the snow."

"I wanted him to help me lift the calf into the tractor box."

"He said it'll be up and walking in a few minutes. We can drive them in."

"We haven't got a few minutes, I want to get it into the warm," he said. It was really snowing in earnest now. Primrose had not yet shown any interest in the calf, but was busy sniffing around the various bodily fluids she had dropped during the birth.

"Lick it dry," I said to her. The calf was shivering. Primrose took no notice.

"Come on," said Gerald, going over to the calf and

trying to pick it up. It slid through his fingers and collapsed in a heap, then struggled unsuccessfully to get to its feet. Primrose was still busy with another damp patch she had found in the grass.

"Give me a hand," said Gerald, and between us we managed to lift the calf and put it in the box on the back of the tractor.

"Bring the cow down," said Gerald, climbing into the tractor seat and driving off down the hill.

"Come on, stupid." I waved my arms at Primrose, who took no notice and seemed to have missed the kidnapping altogether. She gave me an uncomprehending look and returned to snuffling and licking the grass. I smacked my hand on her rump, jarring my wrist painfully. She walked forward towards the holly tree, then arched her back and produced the afterbirth.

Gerald's voice drifted up the hill.

"Come on. What are you doing?"

Primrose got very excited about the afterbirth and started to eat it...this may be very natural, but it's pretty disgusting, and very frustrating if you are worried about her baby shivering, motherless, in the calving pen.

"Go on, you stupid animal," I shouted, rushing towards her. She turned and swung her head menacingly at me. I stopped.

Ernie, as usual, was right; we should have left the calf with her at least until she had realised it was there, and hers. Now she was defending the afterbirth.

"Bring the calf back," I shouted to Gerald, who was now halfway up the field on his feet. "She won't move."

Gerald turned back to the barn, then re-appeared carrying two sticks. At last he was giving me the cow-driving stick I had always wanted.

The snow was swirling thickly around us as we beat Primrose down the hill and into the calving pen. From then on things calmed down. She sniffed the calf, and to our great relief started to lick it dry, talking quietly to it as she did so. The calf struggled to its feet after about three attempts, and managed to find the udder. All was well. We had our first live calf.

It lived for nine days, getting sicker and sicker while the vet injected antibiotics, until finally, five hours before it died, he diagnosed meningitis. Apparently there is only one antibiotic which crosses the blood/brain barrier, and it wasn't the one he had been giving.

I'd had enough of cattle breeding. For nine days I had nursed the calf, watching it get more and more miserable, and when it finally died I had to let Primrose stay with it for a while, so that she would understand that it was dead. Gerald, as usual, was at work when this happened, and consequently missed the sight of me standing with my arm round Primrose's neck, both of us looking down at the dead calf, with tears rolling down my face as I tried to comfort her, while she talked to it and tried to make it get up.

Hippo and Gormless bulled again, and the A.I. man began suggesting that it was beginning to look as if we wouldn't manage to get them back in calf, at which point Gerald got very disheartened and completely lost interest in the cows.

In fact, he seemed to lose interest in the farm as a whole. I tried to persuade him to sell the cows and cut his losses, but he got angry with me and said he didn't want to discuss it at the moment.

"If we we're going to do that we might as well sell

the farm, and go back to London," he said.

I shut up. I would dearly have loved to see the back of the cows, but I didn't want to leave Warren Hanger.

We were still well into the grip of winter, and when we woke one morning to find three inches of snow, Gerald decided that he would stay up in town for the next few days, rather than struggle to work each morning. I was surprised to find his absence a relief. He'd been so grumpy since the calf died, that I had been having to watch what I said.

Since he seemed to have 'gone off' the farm, and it was virtually all I had to talk about, our evenings were becoming increasingly silent. Gerald would go straight into the sitting room to watch television after supper, and then proceed to 'channel hop' at such speed, that sitting in there with him was very uncomfortable.

I had set the word processor up in the corner of the kitchen, where it was warm, and tried once more to write something, anything...I even tried poetry.

The poems were pathetically juvenile, full of contrived rhymes, and ended up in the dustbin.

When the snow melted off the drive two days later, and Gerald came home, he seemed in a slightly better mood, and even said he was looking forward to the lambing.

CHAPTER THIRTY ONE

If we had thought January was cold, February made us think again. Every day became a battle with the elements, leaving me exhausted and numb by the time darkness fell. The temperatures reached record lows. Iron gates around the farm tore the fingers and palms off my gloves, as they froze to the rails. I had never been so cold in my life, and each day seemed to hold another nasty painful joke up its sleeve for me. Even the silage, which we were now feeding to the cows, froze solid in the clamp, and trying to cut it out with a spade was pure exhausting torture.

The water froze in the field troughs, and the ice had to be broken every morning before the sheep could drink; then again in the evening, after it had been re-frozen by the east wind which screamed in straight from Siberia. This ice was about two inches thick and the only way I could break it was with a club hammer - an operation which left small ice floes bobbing about in the trough and splashes of freezing water soaking into my jeans, putting my legs in severe danger of frostbite.

The water supply to the cows in the barn completely froze up, and for four days I had to carry water to them from the house. Cows drink gallons of water, especially when they are eating dry food like hay and cattle cake, and my entire day seemed to be devoted to ensuring this supply. I would finally trudge back up the hill as dusk fell, and the rooks cawed overhead, riding the bitter wind back to their roost. The light would be almost gone as I reached the house, the last

271

crescent of a blood red sun, which carried no warmth at all, sinking out of sight behind the Downs.

A hot bath was the best way of warming up when I came in, if I could summon the energy, but it made my chilblains itch.

Gerald finally bought miles of garden hose for a temporary supply to the cattle shed but, it was almost more trouble than it was worth as it had to be dragged into the barn and covered with straw between trough-filling sessions. He promised to re-route the supply underground before the next winter.

It was while I was struggling to get a barrowload of silage from the clamp one morning that Conor walked into the bottom yard. Festooned as I was with jerseys, ragged gloves, scarves and a totally unflattering black woollen balaclava that even the most desperate of bank robbers would have spurned, I couldn't have been caught at more of a disadvantage.

Snatching off the balaclava, I slid down the silage clamp, stumbling as I landed on the concrete. Conor caught my elbow and steadied me.

"I've brought your logs. Is Ernie around? He can help me unload them. I've left the trailer up at the top. I thought you'd want them near the house."

"Ernie only comes on Wednesdays. Can you just tip them out?"

He looked at my spade and the half-filled wheelbarrow.

"Do you have to do this every day? That's no job for a woman."

"I know, but I have refused to learn how to drive the tractor...it's my fault, really."

"I don't think your husband realises what he asks of you. Did you always want to farm?"

"I never wanted to farm; somehow this is one of Gerald's hobbies which I seem to have ended up doing for him. When we came down here I thought I'd try my hand at being a writer, but somehow there doesn't seem to have been time."

"A writer?"

"Yes, stupid idea. Playing at farming was all right at first, a bit of a laugh, then things started to go wrong with the cows. We have now lost all our calves, and two of the cows are proving impossible to get in calf again. I wish Gerald would get rid of them. But you didn't come down here to listen to me moaning. I'll come up to the top yard and show you where to tip the logs."

I was feeling so scruffy that I wanted Conor to go. I wanted him to stay and talk, but I wanted him to go. I suddenly felt terribly lonely.

"The trailer doesn't tip. Do you want me to stack them for you? It's no bother; I'll put them beside the others in the top barn. You don't need to drag all the way up the hill, I can see you're busy. Would you like a hand with that?"

"No, no, I've nearly finished," I lied. "What about paying you for the logs? I could pop the money round next time I'm passing, if that's all right."

"That'll be fine...I'd work on him again about getting rid of the cows. They're not giving you anything back for all that hard work."

"I'll try. Thanks for the logs; you must let me buy you a drink next time we meet in the pub...for saving me in the woods on Boxing Day. I took your advice, and didn't tell anyone."

"Not even your husband?"

"No."

He gave me a long look, a half smile, then suddenly dropped his eyes and turned away.

"Till we meet in the pub, then," he said.

I watched him stride out of the yard and away up the track, hitching his shoulders as he turned up his coat collar against the wind.

That evening I sat in the sitting room with Gerald, and watched half a minute each of four separate television programmes in rotation for ten minutes, before I could stand it no longer. My brain was becoming totally scrambled as I watched a pride of lions stalking a pregnant wildebeeste through the back streets of Liverpool on a jumbo jet filled with screaming passengers.

"Gerald, for God's sake!" I yelled. I hadn't meant to yell, but was trying to be heard above the screams of the passengers and the laughing of the hyenas surrounding the lions and their kill.

"What?" He jumped. "What's the matter?"

"I was going to ask you the same thing. You don't seem to be able to concentrate on anything for more than a few seconds at a time. Is something worrying you?"

"Of course not. What are you talking about?"

"Can we turn that off and have a proper conversation, please, Gerald? I need to talk to you about the farm; well, the cows."

"Oh! Not that again. I'll make a decision about the cows when I'm ready."

I lost my temper.

"Well, I've made a decision about the cows now. I'm not looking after them any more."

"Oh, don't be silly. It's only because it's a bit cold at the moment that things have got difficult... I'll see if

Ernie can do any more to give you a hand until the weather warms up, but I can't afford to pay him much more."

"Gerald, you don't seem to be hearing me. I don't want to look after them any more, ever. Cows are stupid. Having cows is stupid. In fact, I am almost at the stage of saying either they go, or I'll have to... I can't cope, it's too cold. You're not being fair... Will you turn that bloody television off!"

He did. He turned it off and threw the remote control onto an empty armchair.

"Jill, I don't need this. I've had a hard day's work and I just need to relax. In fact, I'm going to bed."

He was asleep by the time I had calmed down enough to go upstairs.

The following morning was tense.

"Have you thought about what I said?" I finally had to ask.

"I told you, I'll sort something out about the cows."

"What does that mean? Sell them?"

"I don't know...those are really good pedigrees. I probably wouldn't be able to get such good ones again."

"Gerald, the stupid things are barren; well, half of them are; they're useless to you."

"All right...I'll get rid of them. There, now are you satisfied?"

"Yes. Do you mean..."

"I've said I'll get rid of them and that's the end of the matter. Now I've got a train to catch."

Did he mean all of them, or just Hippo and Gormless? Oh well, never mind. Losing half of them was better than none at all, though it would make little difference to my day's schedule.

As I plodded down the hill with the dogs, I was trying to fight off a deep depression which had settled over me as Gerald's car had disappeared out of the drive. The wind had swung round to the west during the night, and for the first morning for ages there was no frost. Though the temperature was only marginally above freezing it felt positively warm; my spirits should have been lifting, not dropping.

I wondered if I could find time to go to London and spend a day with Max. He was always happy, he would cheer me up.

With the animals fed, I called the dogs away from a fast and furious rat hunt behind the barn, where they had excavated huge quantities of earth in an attempt to get at them under the building. They came reluctantly, spitting out mouthfuls of clay and clawing at straws which had caught between their teeth, and we went back to the house for coffee.

I phoned Max to discuss going up to see him, but his next two weekends were 'spoken for'. We chatted for a while and I began to feel better.

"How's Gerald?" he asked.

"Oh, he's fine...I'm trying to persuade him to get rid of some of the cows."

"I saw him the other evening; was he staying in town?"

"He didn't mention seeing you," I said.

"No, he didn't. We were in the car...they were just coming out of Finchley Central tube station...erm."

"What d'you mean 'erm'... and what d'you mean 'they'?"

"Well...well, I'm sure it was all right. He was with that secretary...erm, Hazel."

"Oh...yes, he did stay in town for a couple of days

when we had that really freezing weather. I expect Hazel and Alan had invited him round for supper."

"Of course, that must have been it. Anyway, Mum, I must go now, I'll come down and see you soon. Take care."

"And you...'bye, darling."

Why hadn't Gerald mentioned Hazel and Alan?

I felt restless, and rang Erica.

"Fancy a trip to Chichester?" I asked.

"What, now?"

"Yes. I need to get out; this cold weather has kept me pinned down for too long. I want to wear one of my new coats and a fancy pair of boots. I'm sick of ragged anoraks and wellingtons. I need to browse in some shops and have a civilised lunch somewhere nice and warm."

"Sounds good to me. I'll meet you there. That little car park in the middle, what...12.30 ish?" Erica said.

"Fine...see you later."

I fed the dogs, rinsed the mud out of their eyes with eye lotion, and changed into some proper clothes. Picking my way carefully across the yard, which was becoming muddy as the frost melted, I climbed into the car and wiped my boots clean again with some tissues, before setting off.

Erica was there before me.

"Goodness, you look smart," she said, taking in the black leather coat, and black boots with tan tops.

"It's a joy to get out of wellies," I said.

We had a relaxed wander round lovely warm department stores which smelled of expensive perfumes. I inhaled deeply.

"Are you all right?" Erica asked.

"Can you smell silage and cow dung?"

"What?...No."

"Neither can I," I said.

After lunch, more shopping, then an indulgent tea with toasted tea-cakes, and scones and cream. We were making our bloated way back to the car park, when Erica remembered there was a book she wanted from Hammicks.

I was browsing along a shelf as she queued to pay when she reached over and nudged me, then pointed to the back cover of a book which the man in front of her had just bought.

"Doesn't that look like your mystery Irishman?"

I looked as the man left the counter and headed for the stairs, but he turned the book around.

"He's Conor something, isn't he? What's his surname? I'll ask at the desk."

"Don't be silly, Erica; of course it wasn't him."

"What's his name?"

"Ahern, but it's not him. Come on. I'm going to be doing the animals in the dark at this rate." But Erica was already at the desk.

"Have you anything by Conor Ahern?" she asked.

"Can you spell the surname, please?" the assistant asked.

She tapped the name into her computer, then shook her head.

"No, sorry, do you have any more to go on - any titles?"

"No, sorry," said Erica. "I must have made a mistake."

"Come on, it's getting late." I led the way down the stairs.

"What happened to the book you were going to write?" Erica asked, as we left the shop. "How are you getting on with the word processor?"

"I'm not. There doesn't seem to be time any more, by evening I'm brain dead - and anyway, Gerald is at home then. I've written a few letters on it, but he says the noise of the printer is irritating."

"Are things all right between you two? He was all over you at Christmas, but you don't seem too happy."

I tried to describe the situation between myself and Gerald, but as it didn't really make sense to me I found it impossible to tell her - it just sounded as if I was whingeing. It wasn't Gerald's fault that the calf had had meningitis...or that the other three had died. Nor was it his fault that the old ewe had died, and the chicken deaths were all down to my dogs.

I ended up by telling her, lamely, that we were not meant to be farmers, but Gerald was having difficulty accepting the fact, and was feeling depressed. He had gone into it all with such high expectations.

"You're going to be lambing soon. How does he feel about the sheep, now the cows have gone 'pear-shaped'?"

I laughed at the picture this remark conjured up.

"He hasn't shown much interest in them lately, but I think they all look well - and pregnant. A trouble-free lambing might cheer him up a bit. I hope so."

We had reached our cars.

"Give my love to Gerald, and to Max when you next speak to him," Erica called as she unlocked her car.

I waved back and set off home, to exchange my finery for my working rags. Cinderella, eat your heart out, I thought, but I felt better, a bit of civilisation had done me good. 'Some day my Prince will arrive,' I hummed, before suddenly realising I wasn't imagining Gerald in this role.

CHAPTER THIRTY TWO

"So much for having better luck with the sheep," I muttered to Huggy.

I was standing in the ewes' field looking down at the obviously defunct body of another one of the three old ewes which Gerald had brought back from Oxford. She was very wet. It looked as if she had been lying there for most of the night. There was no visible indication as to why she had died.

Remembering Cheap and Nasty's caesarian entry into the world, I looked for signs of movement from her unborn lamb, but the stillness was absolute. I was relieved in a way; I had no wish for my first assisted delivery to be a caesarian done with a kitchen knife. I went indoors to phone the kennels to come and fetch the carcase, but first I phoned Erica.

"Oh, bad luck," she said.

"Do you think I should have a post-mortem done?"

"No, waste of time...and money. Probably old age. Dying is what sheep do best; it's rarely worth finding out why, unless several more keel over. How do they look?"

"Fine, as far as I can tell."

I arranged for the kennels to collect her. That only left one of the old ewes bought for their fantastic pedigrees; the one we had named Slit Ear, for obvious reasons. Sometime during her youth one of her ear tags had been ripped out. She was quite a sweet old thing and I was glad it wasn't her body I had found.

Gerald was very angry when I told him of this latest

death, as he walked in that evening.

"Why did she die? Are we going to lose all the sheep as well now? Don't you check them regularly? Couldn't you see that she was ill? We'll have to have a post-mortem."

"We can't. I've already sent her to the kennels. Erica said..."

"I don't care what your sister said; what does she know about sheep? Donald does all the farming there."

"You're obviously not prepared to listen to me at the moment. We'll talk when you've calmed down. Eat your supper."

He snatched a tray and took his meal into the sitting room. I stayed in the kitchen rather than sit with him while he sulked. I tried to remember whether the old ewe had seemed 'off colour' the previous evening, but they had all rushed at me when I delivered their supper. As Erica had said, it was probably old age.

In the end we didn't talk about it, and Gerald didn't mention the old ewe again, but after this little altercation my heart sank two days later when I took some food out to the sheep and one of them didn't get up and come running down to the trough.

I walked up across the field. She obviously wasn't dead; in fact, it looked as if she was in labour, but it was a bit too early for that. As I got closer I saw it was Slit Ear, and when I reached her I could see that something was horribly wrong. Walking round to her rear end I found what looked appallingly like the picture of a prolapsed uterus in the sheep instruction manual, which Gerald had insisted I read.

It started to rain as I tried to get her to her feet. She obviously needed a vet and I wanted her under cover. I managed to get her up, but she wouldn't walk and

281

quickly lay down again.

Rushing indoors, I rang the vet who was out on call, but his receptionist promised he would be with me as soon as possible.

I looked for the sheep book, then remembered Gerald had taken it to show to Hazel. I couldn't imagine her wanting to read it; she obviously had a stronger stomach than I'd credited her with. Should I ring Hazel and get her to talk me through emergency procedures for dealing with prolapsing ewes? A gust of wind spattered rain against the kitchen window as I discarded this idea. I was on my own... again.

I collected a sheet and a clean towel which I ran under the warm tap to dampen it, and headed back to the field.

Pushing Slit Ear to her feet again, I gently pushed the prolapsed part of the uterus back inside her, using the damp towel, then held the towel in place with the sheet, which I took up each side of her, crossing the ends over her shoulders, then tying them in a bow under her chin. Amazingly, this was still in place when the vet arrived an hour later, though she was still standing out in the field, as I hadn't managed to get her to move.

We walked up to the field and he looked across at the flock as I opened the gate for him.

"Which one is it? " he asked.

"The one with its ass in a sling," I replied, thinking this was a pretty dumb question. Slit Ear was the only sheep in the field wearing a pretty yellow flowered sheet.

He laughed as he pulled three lengths of baler twine out of the pocket of his waxed jacket. Then, having examined her, he proceeded to tie up her naughty bits with a complicated cat's cradle of loops and knots. The end result of which was that Slit Ear, even more convinced that she couldn't move, was still standing in the same spot half an hour after he had gone.

As it was now raining steadily I decided to try again to get her under cover. This operation took half an hour, with me half-lifting her one step at a time. Once in the stable in the top yard she collapsed, turned her nose up to proffered food and prepared to die.

"No, petal, please, I don't want another evening of Gerald shouting at me. You are not to die." I rattled the bucket of sheep nuts under her nose and she turned her head away.

I tried her twice more at hourly intervals but she was still refusing food, and wouldn't get up. I was getting stressed and popped a small brandy into my coffee to calm me down. Then rang the vet for advice.

He asked if I had tried feeding her with milk and beaten eggs, and I had to admit that this had not occurred to me as sustaining food for a sheep.

"Give it a try," he said.

I broke two of our precious brown eggs into a pint of milk - the hens had virtually stopped laying at the moment - stirred it well, and carried it across to the stable.

"Come on, old girl, get up," I pleaded.

She gave me a look which I translated as 'can't you let me die in peace?'.

I knelt on the floor in front of her and offered the bowl of milk. She turned her head away. I tried tipping a little into her mouth while she swung her head about and coughed. Then, afraid I would get some into her lungs and really kill her, I got up. Maybe she would like it warmed up a bit.

I went back into the kitchen and while I was

warming the mixture, I had a swig of brandy out of the bottle to warm me. There is something very decadent about swigging brandy out of a bottle, especially when it's Gerald's precious Remy Martin. On that thought, I poured a generous slug into Slit Ear's mixture, and took it back out to her. She instantly swung her head away when she saw the dish I was carrying. I had brought a large spoon with me, and tried spooning some into the corner of her mouth while she spat it out just as fast.

I gave up and put the bowl to one side on the floor, while I rose from my knees. The fumes of the warm brandy must have reached her nostrils in the draught from the door. Slit Ear gave a couple of sniffs and struggled to her feet, then took two steps over to the dish, slurped up all the egg mixture and frantically licked the dish dry. I gave her a cuddle, but she pushed me out of the way as she chased the empty dish round the stable. Rescuing it from her before it broke, I went and mixed another pint, using the last of the eggs - but left out the brandy.

She was pleased to see the dish back, but when I put it on the floor in front of her, she just sniffed it and turned her head away. I went back for the brandy bottle and poured some in. She drank the lot. Just what I needed, an alcoholic sheep! I took a swig myself to keep her company.

"This looks like fun; are you having a party?" It was the vet. I hadn't heard his car pull up. "I was out this way and I thought I'd just pop in to see how she's doing. She's up, anyway."

"It was the brandy that did it. What about all your pieces of string? I forgot to ask whether I was supposed to remove them eventually," I asked.

"We'll leave her like that until just before she starts

to lamb," he said. "She won't be long now. She should be OK."

"I don't know if we can afford to feed her brandy on a regular basis. You forgot to mention it when you gave me the recipe."

"That's what got her up, was it? Good thinking! Right, you should be all right now. Ring me if you're not happy."

I'm not happy, I thought, but there's not much you can do about it.

Gerald came home with a large bunch of flowers and apologised for being horrid to me over the death of the second old ewe. Rather than spoil the moment I didn't tell him about Slit Ear until later in the evening, when he was nice and relaxed, and gently swirling a brandy around his glass. Even then I didn't tell him what had effected Slit Ear's miraculous recovery.

It was very nice to have him being affectionate again, but never knowing what kind of a mood he would come home in was making me nervous.

"Oh, by the way," I said, "can you ask Hazel if she's finished with that book about sheep? We're going to need it any minute when lambing starts. If she's really interested we must invite them down again to see the babies."

"Them? Oh, them...Alan...yes. I don't know if she...they'd..um, we'll see. Wait till the weather gets better. By the way, Hazel remembered where she thought she'd seen that Irish keeper bloke."

"Really! What, in London?"

"Yes, she swears she saw him signing books in Foyles."

"Oh, then he does have a double. Erica thought she saw a picture of him on the back of a book in

Hammicks the other day, but there's no author called Conor Ahern...she asked the assistant to look him up."

"Why didn't she look at the book?"

"It was going out of the shop under someone else's arm."

"Oh, well, I suppose I'd just better check old Slit Ear before we turn in. Where's the torch?"

CHAPTER THIRTY THREE

A fortnight later Gerald and I turned the cows out into the field near the bottom yard, and converted their winter quarters into a lambing pen, building cosy draught-proof walls with bales of straw. The cows from now on would have to stay out during the day, and spend the nights in the calving pen, which was quite large enough for four of them.

We brought the ewes down to the bottom barn on the Saturday evening, leaving Cheap and Henry to keep each other company. They weren't exactly friends now, but at least they had stopped fighting each other.

After a phone call to the vet to check that it was all right to do so, I undid all the baler twine which was holding Slit Ear together - only just in time. Giving a sigh of relief she wandered over to the warmest corner of the pen and settled down to give birth to twins, with no problems or complications.

I made her some milk, eggs and brandy for being so clever, which amused Gerald until he saw me reach for the brandy.

"That's where it's all been going, is it? I thought it was you."

I ignored this slur on my character.

"Don't knock it...it's a small price to pay for two healthy lambs. Think of the pedigrees."

There were three more ewes marked with red crayon, they would be next; the other three had green patches on their backs from the change of crayon two weeks later.

We waited with Slit Ear until her lambs were up and had fed from her, then went indoors to warm up.

"Maybe we are going to have better luck with the sheep," Gerald said hopefully.

I seized the opportunity once more to try to persuade him to sell the cows, I could sense he was wavering.

"We'll see," he said.

"If you check the sheep last thing, I'll set the alarm and have a look at them around 3am," I said.

"Is that really necessary? The alarm will wake me as well and you know how difficult I find it to get back to sleep."

"I'll go into the spare room if you like. Maybe I should remind you that these are your sheep and your hobby. I'm not suggesting a foray into a cold winter night just for the fun of it."

"Right! If you're going to be like that, I'll do it."

"Do what?" I asked, not sure whether he meant moving into the spare room, or checking the sheep at 3am.

"Check the bloody sheep at some ungodly hour."

"OK. you can always call me if you need some help."

"Don't worry, I won't bother you...*I'll* move into the spare room."

Somehow he made the statement sound like a threat. Was I getting over-sensitive? The new Gerald who'd arrived with the bunch of flowers seemed to be slipping away again.

I stayed up until midnight, then, muffled in coat and scarf, I took the torch and went down to the bottom barn. It was a cold, but clear night, with a nearly full moon, I hardly needed the torch. Using my ears I followed the progress of a fox which was cutting through Connor's wood. Every thirty seconds or so it gave a triple bark, each time from a little further away.

An owl screeched from an ancient oak tree just inside the wood, and was answered by another from further down the valley. I stood for a moment or two, leaning on a gate half way down the hill drinking in the timeless peace. There was no light pollution here to dim the stars.

The fox barked again, down in the bottom of the valley, and I imagined it crossing the road by the old stone bridge. London was another world...I could never go back. I resolved to make more of an effort not to irritate Gerald. Though not quite sure why, I was constantly getting the feeling that I did.

The barn gave a welcome feeling of comfortable silence, broken only by the rustle of straw and the contented burping of the ewes as they regurgitated another mouthful of cud to chew.

Slit Ear's babies were asleep. She checked both my hands to see if I was carrying anything remotely alcoholic, glanced at her lambs, then put her chin on the straw and dozed again.

I shone the torch over each of the ewes, not wanting to put the overhead light on and disturb them. They all looked completely relaxed; I checked their water supply and went back to the house.

In the morning I took a cup of tea in to Gerald, before going down to look at the ewes again. He was sound asleep, but roused as I put the tea down on his bedside table.

"Wha?...What time is it?"

"Seven-thirty. Was everything all right?"

"What?...The ewes! Shit! That bloody alarm didn't go off!"

Be nice, I was saying to myself. Remember you were going to be nice.

"Don't worry, I'll go down now," I said.

"I'll get dressed. I'll be down in a minute."

I took the dogs with me to the bottom yard, to find a scene very different from the peace of the previous night. The ewes seemed to be mobbing one of their number and when I pushed them out of the way, I could see that she was lying exhausted from what looked like hours of struggle, trying to give birth to a lamb whose front legs were back.

Only the head was born, the tongue hanging out was black and the eyes open and staring. I tried to pull the lamb out, but the book had said I should push the head back in and try to find the legs and pull them out first. Smearing lubricating fluid all over my hand and arm, I attempted to do this, but the poor ewe had been in this state for so long that any natural lubrication had dried up and the lamb was stuck fast. I wasn't strong enough to move it. I was squirting the fluid all around the dead lamb's neck when Gerald arrived.

"Oh, good, another one."

I was furious at the unnecessary suffering the ewe had endured.

"No! Not good! You careless bastard! You can't do anything properly where the animals are concerned, can you? This poor little ewe has been in agony for hours. The lamb is dead. You try and get it out...I can't budge it." I wanted to cry but I was too angry with him. We might have saved it if he'd checked them as he should have done.

Gerald's extra muscle, and more lubrication, finally

extracted the lamb and the ewe groaned and rolled flat on her side.

"Why can't anything on this farm give birth properly? I suppose we're going to lose all the lambs now," Gerald fumed.

"We might have saved this one if you'd checked them."

"Don't start nagging me again. I couldn't help it if the alarm clock didn't go off."

He hadn't set it, but there didn't seem to be any point in mentioning it now. I carried a bucket of water to the little ewe. She raised her head gratefully and drank nearly all of it.

"Shouldn't we make her get up?" Gerald asked.

"Leave her alone. If you want to do something useful you can feed the others."

I picked up the dead lamb, and, collecting the spade, went round the barn to the burial ground. The ground had frozen so hard during the previous cold spell that I couldn't dig much of a grave, so I put a cairn of stones on the top to deter predators.

I called the dogs away from a rat hunt and went back to the house. I hadn't had a cup of tea yet, and I didn't feel like talking to Gerald for a while - he was still in the barn.

He came back into the kitchen and, without speaking to me, picked up the kettle and was filling it at the sink when three ramblers walked past the window. One of them saw him and waved.

"Right! That does it!" he exploded. "I've had enough of this. We're going to sell this place and go back to civilisation." He slammed the kettle down on top of the Aga and droplets of splashed water boiled and sizzled.

"What!" My heart sank. I was all for giving up trying to farm, but not for returning to London. Noise, fumes, soulless walks in the park. I would hate it, the dogs would hate it. And what about Cheap?

I tried to lighten the atmosphere. "I couldn't take Cheap to London, his wool would get all smutty." It didn't work.

"You're mad - that sheep can go to the butcher with the rest of them. You've never had the right attitude to livestock farming."

I ignored that. "Gerald, I don't want to move back to London. Couldn't we find a cottage somewhere - somewhere near here?"

"After all your complaining about the cold and the mud, I'd have thought you'd be only too pleased to get back to 'town'."

The windows rattled slightly in the concussion from an explosion in the chalk quarry on the downs ten miles away. Conor's pheasants squawked alarm calls and I wondered if the white bird was part of the chorus.

"Anyway," he said, "it's obvious that everything here is too much for you. I've tried to stop irritating you but you are still nagging me about this place. You're always tired and I'm sick of commuting every day, this whole idea was a mistake. I'm putting the farm on the market and I'm going back to London...you can please yourself."

"What?" Suddenly I was shaking and deeply confused. What did he mean, 'I could please myself'? Was he trying to push me into leaving him? Why? He was implying that it was partly my fault things hadn't worked out according to his expectations. Was it my fault? Where would I go? I would have to find somewhere to live...and a job. I had three dogs and a sheep to support. Homes in the country were expensive. Sale of the farm wouldn't cover purchasing a London flat and a country cottage. My mind raced in circles.

"What's happening to us?" I said.

"You've changed - all you do nowadays is moan and nag me about the animals. It's no wonder I'm sick of farming."

"That's not fair," I wailed. Did I nag all the time?...Thoughts charged through my head, but no words would come.

"Fair or not, we'll get rid of this place; it's really been nothing but trouble... after all your whingeing I'd have thought you'd be pleased. And there's no privacy here!" he shouted, waving his fist at another startled rambler.

"I need to think," I said.

Calling the dogs, I put my coat on and went out of the back door. Huggy dived behind the woodpile after a mouse, knocking down several logs which rolled across the yard. I picked them up and re-stacked them, feeling numb. The last hands to touch these logs had been Conor's. What was I going to do?

I took a deep breath and straightened up, looking down the valley to the misty Downs in the distance. I wasn't going back to London; whatever it took, I was going to try to stay in this area, with or without Gerald. A small voice in the back of my mind was trying to tell me that perhaps I didn't love him any more. Did I really want to spend the rest of my life with him? He and I needed to discuss this rationally.

I changed my mind about going for a walk and, shutting the dogs into their paddock, went back to the house. The scullery door hadn't latched as I went out, and he didn't hear me come in - he was on the phone.

"No, darling – I've set things in motion. Luckily there was a 'cock-up' with one of the sheep this morning, which gave me the opportunity to give the situation a bit of a push."

I went cold - who was 'Darling'? This row was a set up. The devious bastard! I backed out of the scullery door quietly, and tiptoed across the yard to the dog paddock. I needed to sort my mind out before I made any sudden move now. Who the hell was 'Darling'?

I opened the paddock gate and Huggy bounced up at my leg. "Let's hunt," he said, and took Rudi and Flicka down the hill towards the bottom yard. I followed them, trying to form a plan of my own.

The zig-zag shape of a grey heron flapped lazily above the wood, seemingly untroubled by the two crows who tumbled crazily about it as they mobbed the large bird, and tried to drive it away from the area. I wondered idly why crows mob herons; they don't compete for the same food or nesting space. I realised I was reaching for any odd thought to distract my mind from the current overwhelming crisis.

When I reached the bottom barn the dogs were round at the back, trying to excavate the dead lamb I had just buried.

"Leave it!" I yelled, and put them on leads. I checked the ewes again; the little ewe was still lying down, but with her head up and her feet tucked under her. She looked much better.

I didn't want to go back to the house yet, and the dogs were fidgeting on their leads. Opening the gate which led out of the yard to the last of our fields before the woods began, I unclipped them and they shot off ahead of me.

At the bottom of the hill we crossed the road, round about where I had imagined the fox crossing on the previous night, and climbed the steep track through the chestnut copse on the other side of the valley. I had a sudden insane urge to just keep walking west ... forever.

The sound of a chain saw suddenly buzzed ahead of us, and on the brow of the hill a car was parked on the side of the track, the driver's door wide open. As we drew near a white bullet hurled itself from the driving seat, and told us in no uncertain terms to go away: Flicka and Rudi did, only Huggy stood his ground... rather uncertainly. It was Sid's elderly Jack Russell bitch, guarding his car for him as he felled the young chestnut trees ready for fence posts, and the chestnut fencing which was so prevalent in the area.

Sid spent a lot of his time out in these woods, most of it under a tarpaulin lean-to shelter where he split the straight trunks and bundled up the staves ready to be wired together as fencing. He looked up and shouted at Emily to get back in the car; she turned sulkily and waddled back to her place on the front seat, too many packets of crisps at the pub accounting for her portly figure.

I waved, he grinned and waved back, then pulled the starting cord on his chain saw again.

This was all very well, but it was not getting my future sorted out. I called up the dogs and turned for home.

CHAPTER THIRTY FOUR

Gerald was in the bottom yard, standing by the barn, as the dogs and I crossed the field, and I put them on their leads before opening the yard gate. They were already sniffing the air towards the graveyard. As Gerald was here he could dig a deeper grave for the lamb.

"Where've you been? I was worried," he said.

"Were you?" I didn't want to talk to him at the moment.

"Of course. You just vanished in the middle of our discussion."

"It didn't feel like a discussion."

"What does that mean?"

"Look, I'm sorry I shouted at you about the lamb. I was upset because the little ewe had been suffering all that time. Can you bury the lamb properly? The ground was too hard for me to dig, and the dogs were after the body."

He glared at the dogs who were used to it by now and took no notice.

"Those dogs cause half the problems around here – can't you re-home them somewhere?"

"No." I walked over to the ewes' pen. The little one who'd just lost her lamb was on her feet and eating hay. The other two, who were marked with red crayon, and would have been mated around the same time, looked quite relaxed. Gerald had followed me and I found his hovering presence irritating.

"I'm going up to the shop," I said.

"It's Sunday."

"Oh, yes."

"What did you want?" he asked.

"A bar of chocolate - it doesn't matter. I'll go and make breakfast."

"I'm serious about selling this place, Jill."

"I know."

"Well?"

"If that's really what you want, there's nothing I can do about it. I had enough of fighting in my first marriage. I don't want to start again."

"You mean you would consider moving back to London?" he looked worried.

Bastard! I thought. I was playing him at his own game, but I wasn't enjoying it, and I still needed a plan. Erica and Donald might let me stay with them while I sorted my life out - at least there would be room there for Cheap. All I knew at the moment was that I didn't think I could go on living with a man who seemed to be considering replacing me with 'Darling'.

"I don't seem to have any alternative," I said. "We should never have left in the first place. We were happy there - something seems to have gone wrong between us since we came down here; and if we'd stayed in London I wouldn't have fallen in love with this little patch of England. That's what will make leaving so hard, not the animals...trying to farm was a silly idea. Breakfast will be ready in about half an hour."

I went back to the house via the hen house, tying the dogs to the fence while I collected their production for that morning - one solitary egg.

"This seems to be a low point in your lives as well, girls; I wonder where you'll end up," I said. The hens murmured comfortingly as they scratched about in the straw of their palace, and in the distance I heard the tractor start up as Gerald went to re-bury the lamb.

I was just laying rashers of bacon in the frying pan, and feeling very sorry for myself, when the phone rang; wiping my hands I picked it up.

"Oh, hello, it's Mrs Arnham here, Nutkin's owner. I've been meaning to ring you for ages, but you know how it is. I thought I'd better just let you know that she didn't have any puppies."

I swallowed hard to try to get rid of a huge lump which had lodged in my throat, and forced my voice to sound normal.

"I'm so sorry. I'll return the stud fee. Let me have your address."

"No, no, we don't want it back, I just thought you ought to know that your dog is probably infertile, in case you were thinking of mating him again."

"Well, Mrs Arnham, it's very kind of you to let me know. Thank you very much."

"That's perfectly all right...we're rather relieved in a way. Puppies might have been a bit of a nuisance. Some friends of ours have asked us to join them for a long cruise on their yacht."

"Well, I hope you have a very nice holiday."

"Thank you. Goodbye." She hung up. It was another world.

I looked at Huggy, stretched out blissfully on his bed in front of the Aga.

"You're infertile," I told him.

"I love you too," his eyes said as his tail thumped twice on the muddy bean bag.

My mind returned to 'Darling'; there had been a faint smell of perfume on the leather coat Gerald had given me for Christmas...had 'Darling' modelled it for him? What did she look like? Where did he find her ... and when? I tried to remember when I had first thought our relationship was cooling off.

None of that matters, my mind was trying to tell me. Face the fact that, the way he is now, you'd be happier without him.

The trouble is, I told my mind, I don't have any money. All my savings had gone to solicitors when I divorced David; and as he had been deeply in debt, I had come out of that marriage with Max, my clothes, the dogs and nothing else.

Smoke began to drift from the grill. I snatched the pan out and discarded the black slices of toast into the bin. The bacon was looking a bit crisp too. The scullery door banged as I rescued the rashers, and put more bread under the grill.

"Something's burning," he said. "I've re-buried the lamb, these little sods won't be able to dig it up now."

"Are you really serious about selling Warren Hanger, Gerald? Couldn't we just get rid of the animals and let the land for grazing? There are plenty of people with horses around here."

"Are you happy with me?" he asked.

"That's an odd question... I could ask if you are happy with me," I countered.

"Well, as you said, things seem to have changed between us. I'm not sure if I know you any more."

I was suddenly tired of playing his game.

"What exactly are you getting at, Gerald? Have you fallen for somebody else?"

He went scarlet.

"Of course I haven't; whatever makes you say that? I'm just worried that you don't seem too happy any more."

"I'm not, but perhaps it would be better to leave this for today...I'm feeling a bit mixed up. We'll talk about it tomorrow evening when you get home. I want to get things straight in my mind," I said. I wanted to talk to Erica before then.

We were polite to each other for the rest of the day, and I did the 3am check of the ewes, but none of them were lambing.

The post the next morning contained a bill for the logs which Conor had brought us. Gerald wrote a cheque and I pushed it, and the bill, into my handbag, meaning to get a stamp from the post office to send the payment to Conor. I rang Erica and arranged to meet her in the Royal Oak for a drink at lunchtime.

We took our drinks into a quiet corner of the bar.

"What's the problem?" she said. "I can see that there is one."

I told her that Gerald wanted to sell the farm.

"I'm not really surprised," she said. "It was pretty obvious he'd got sick of the animal side of things, but does that mean you'll go back to London? You're not going to be very happy about that, are you?"

"No. I hate the idea. I don't know what to do. In fact, I think this has all come about because Gerald is having an affair - at least I think he is. I heard him talking on the phone to someone called 'Darling', and he looked horribly guilty when I asked him outright if there was someone else. He denied it."

"Really! Does he know that you heard him on the phone? You should tell him. Ask him who she is."

"No, not yet."

"You really are a wimp, Jill. Jolly well let him know that you know, and take it from there; he'll soon drop her if he thinks it's getting complicated."

"It's not that simple...I don't know if I want to spend the rest of my life with him, after all."

"You're not thinking of another divorce?"

"Don't say it like that; it sounds like my fault, but I suppose, yes, I am. What's the point of fighting for something I don't really want?"

"Where would you go? You'll need a job."

"If it comes to it, and there is a major 'bust-up', could I stay with you and Donald, just till I've found a place of my own? Perhaps I could find a job as farm secretary somewhere, preferably with a cottage included."

"Course you can."

"Oh, that's a great relief...I doubt if it will come to that but it's comforting to know I can.... Now, shall we have a sandwich?"

As we were leaving the pub half an hour later, Conor's Land Rover drew up in the car park and I remembered I had to pay him for the logs. I explained this to Erica. "Do you want to come back in?" I said.

"No, I'd better get back. I'll give you a ring tomorrow, to see what's happening." She waved and drove away as I followed Conor back into the pub, catching up with him at the bar.

"Hello. Would you like a drink?" he asked, smiling.

"Um, well, I really only came back to pay you for the logs, but yes, a half of bitter would be nice."

"I'm celebrating," he said as we carried our drinks over to the table by the window. "I've just completed purchase on the cottage."

"That's marvellous! I'm very pleased for you." I felt like crying, and found myself blurting out, "Gerald wants to sell the farm."

"You're moving?" His face went very still, as he

stared at me.

"It looks like it." My heart jumped: did his expression mean that he would be sorry to see me go? Then it dropped like a stone at his next question.

"Are you selling in one block, or would you consider splitting off the bottom field and the yard? I have plans for starting a small game farm, and that would be an ideal site - right on the edge of my patch."

"I'll ask Gerald for you." Suffocating clouds of depression seemed to roll over me.

"You don't want to leave, do you? I've never seen you look this miserable before, not even that morning I found you frozen to the top of the silage clamp."

I smiled at this picture.

"You're right...I am miserable. I love it here and I don't want to move, but I can't force Gerald to stay...he wants to move back to London; he's tired of the travelling."

"I'll miss you," he said, and I began to drown in those incredible blue eyes.

The pub door opened and he glanced across the bar.

"Ah! Here she is," he said.

I looked up - the black-haired woman was coming through the door, looking stunning as usual. I felt as if I were riding a roller coaster. Pushing my chair back I began to get up.

"I'd better go; I've got ewes to check," I said.

He put his hand on my arm and all the blood in my body rushed to that one tingling spot.

"No, stay and meet her," he said.

She smiled and came over to us.

"Hello, Niamh," he said. "This is Jill Collins from Warren Hanger Farm - Jill, this is my sister Niamh."

I sat down again with a bump. His sister!...Of

course she was his sister...they were so alike; why hadn't I seen it before?

"Hello, Con." She kissed him.

"Niamh's come to stay for a couple of days; she needs the peace from time to time."

"Let me buy you both a drink," I said. I needed a moment or two to compose my face into a sensible expression.

As I walked away to the bar I heard her asking him how the book was coming along. My head spun. It *was* him on the cover of that book in Hammick's! Jim waved a hand in front of my face as I stood at the bar gazing blankly at the row of optics.

"Hello...anybody in there?" he said.

"Sorry, Jim, um...a gin and tonic and a pint of bitter and ... no, make that two gin and tonics and a pint of bitter."

A famous author? He must be if Hazel had seen him signing books in Foyles. What about the IRA...and the gun? Nothing more than my vivid imagination - dear God, I'd told him that my ambition was to be a writer. I wondered why he didn't write under his own name; maybe the IRA were after him. I told my imagination to shut up, and paid Jim for the drinks.

Setting the glasses down on the table, I looked at him.

"I couldn't help hearing what Niamh just said; are you really an author? - only my sister swore she saw a picture of you on the back of a book someone was carrying the other day, but there was no author listed under Conor Ahern... and Gerald's secretary thinks she saw you signing books in Foyles."

"Your cover's blown, Con," Niamh laughed.

"If it is, it's you who have blown it." He smiled at her.

303

"I'm sorry, I shouldn't interfere," I said.

"It's all right, it's just that in the past I have written one or two rather inflammatory things about my own country, and my publisher suggested a pen-name."

The grandfather clock in the corner of the bar began to chime and I glanced at my watch. I had been away from the ewes for too long. I finished my gin and tonic quickly and stood up, lifting my handbag off the chair.

"I must go – we're in the middle of lambing," I said. Just as I was thinking that this statement sounded rather grand, Niamh asked how many sheep we had. "Eleven," I said, and she laughed.

"Oh! Conor, your cheque." I retrieved it from my bag and handed it to him. "I'll ask Gerald about the field and the bottom yard." With that remark I plunged myself back into misery. "Nice to meet you, Niamh."

Back in the bottom barn all was peaceful. I cuddled Slit Ear's lambs for a while as my mind went round in circles trying to plan some kind of a future.

CHAPTER THIRTY FIVE

That evening Gerald made no mention of Sunday's discussion. I kept waiting for him to open the subject of our future, but he didn't and I began to relax. Maybe this was just a blip in our marriage, and if I didn't push things, probably they would work themselves out and we would be able to stay at Warren Hanger.

After a week of us both avoiding the subject, we were breakfasting on Saturday when he suddenly announced that a lorry was coming in two hours time, to take the cows back to Devon - at considerable financial loss, he emphasised. This bombshell he followed up by saying that he was negotiating the sale of the sheep, to a farmer in Hampshire who'd just gone into breeding Oxford Downs.

I struggled to take this in through a brain 'punch-drunk' with tiredness after a week of doing the 3am check of the ewes. I was beginning to hate the bleeps of the alarm which dragged me from my warm bed to stumble down to the bottom barn, where the ewes grumbled sleepily at me for waking them.

Taking a deep breath, I tried to speak calmly.

"Does that mean you are still thinking of selling the farm, or can we stay here without the animals? That surely would be the best option. We'd have a job to find anywhere else as nice as this."

"I've been looking at some flats in town."

"Without me? Why didn't you tell me all this? I am half of this marriage, you know."

He looked very uncomfortable, and seemed about to

say something, then glanced at the clock.

"Is that thing right? We've got to get the cows up into the top yard so we can load them."

I piled the breakfast dishes in the sink, and pulled on my wellingtons. I suddenly knew I wasn't going to live in a flat in London…the thought appalled me.

As they waited for the lorry, the cows wandered about in the top yard, pulling up the few shrubs they could reach over the low garden wall and leaving an inordinate number of cow-pats on the tarmac. When I tried to say goodbye to them they stared at me as if we'd never met, and eventually ambled up the ramp into the lorry without a backward glance. Gerald went down to the bottom yard to clean out the cowshed, and I went back indoors to wash up the breakfast things.

The telephone rang.

"Hello Mum – how's the lambing going?"

"Max, darling, how are you?"

"I'm fine. Have you got any new babies yet?"

"No, lambing seems to have ground to a halt at the moment and I'm exhausted. It's my own fault, I suppose, but I don't trust Gerald to wake up at 3am."

"Are you doing every night? That's not fair."

"It probably won't be for much longer…Gerald has 'gone off' farming and is selling all the animals…the cows have just this minute gone and the sheep are under notice to quit - not Cheap, of course - and it looks as if we will be selling the farm as well. I don't want to, but he seems determined."

"Why didn't you tell me all this?"

"I've only really just found out myself."

"Will you be coming back to London? You won't want that, will you? The dogs will hate it after all that freedom, and what about Cheap? He'll make an awful mess in an upstairs flat."

"I don't know, darling; Gerald wants to and I don't."

"Is everything all right between you two, Mum?"

"Why do you ask?"

"You don't sound very happy...I don't know if I should say this but...no...never mind."

"Max, you can't stop there - what were you going to say?"

"Well...well, you know I said I'd seen Gerald with Hazel that time?"

"Yes." My mind was racing ahead of the conversation. Hazel was 'Darling'? She could be; yes, she certainly could be...except for Alan.

"Well, they were looking extremely friendly, and then I bumped into Alan yesterday, and when I asked him how Hazel was, he said he didn't know, they'd broken up ages ago."

"Did he say why?"

"You don't sound very surprised, Mum."

"Well, to be honest, I had suspected Gerald might be seeing someone, but Hazel!"

"I'm sorry, Mum, I've probably drawn quite the wrong conclusions. I wasn't going to say anything but..."

"Don't worry, it'll all get sorted out," I told him with more confidence than I felt. We spoke of other things for a while before he rang off with a promise to phone again soon.

I made a coffee and sat with my back against the Aga, both hands clasped round the mug, and as the heat seeped comfortingly through my thick jersey, I realised I was going to lose the Aga as well.

Gerald came roaring up the hill on the tractor,

leaving the engine running as he banged in through the scullery door. The dogs had hysterics, then saw who it was and hid under the dresser.

"Do you have to come in like that?" I said.

"Get scrubbed up quick, and come down, there's a ewe lambing." He grabbed the box containing the necessary sprays and lubricating gels and rushed out again.

I followed him down the hill, breathing in the tractor's diesel fumes which seemed to be hanging at about nose height in the foggy damp air.

As I entered the barn I could see the ewe, head pointing straight up and top lip extended and puckered as she strained. I went over to her.

"Not that one...this one." Gerald was standing beside the other red-marked ewe across the pen.

"And this one... we seem to have synchronized lambing here. D'you think they'd like some music?"

"Stop trying to be funny, Jill, this is serious; there seem to be three feet protruding. Do something."

I wiped my hands with disinfectant and plastered my right hand and arm with lubricating gel.

"Hurry!" he said.

"I am hurrying. Stop panicking." I knelt on the straw behind the ewe. There were indeed three feet, and all of them front ones. This was either a seriously deformed lamb, or a race between twins to be first.

Easing my slippery hand into the ewe I followed the legs back until I found a nose, then it was quite easy to find the odd one out. I lay down so that I could get my arm in almost to the elbow, and between the ewe's pushes, tried to move the third leg back, whilst pulling gently on the other two as she pushed. Nothing much seemed to be moving.

"Do you know what you're doing?" Gerald said. "Shall I get the vet?"

"Go and have a look at the other one," I said.

He walked over to the other ewe and bent down.

"There's just a tail," he said.

"What?"

"There's only a tail hanging out; can you get over here?"

"No, she'll have to wait. Tell her to stop pushing and pant."

"This isn't a game, Jill."

"I know it's not a bloody game," I ground out as my ewe groaned and gave an enormous heave which delivered one and a half lambs. The second one had a leg back, but the other leg and half the head were delivered. The book said, push it all in and pull the second leg forward, but I took a chance and pulled number two out with a twisting motion and it slithered wetly across its twin, sneezing and shaking its head.

"Look after these while I have a look at her," I said, changing places with Gerald.

"What do you want me to do with them?" He looked helplessly at the soggy newborn jumble.

"If she won't get up, pull them round under her nose so she can lick them dry; help her, there's a towel hanging on that nail over there."

I washed my hands as best I could in a bucket of extraordinarily cold water, poured on more gel and got to work on the other ewe, pushing her child's bottom back in until I could find the hind legs and bring them gently forward one at a time, very aware that one tear from my nails on her uterus could introduce serious infection.

Having got hold of both hind legs, it didn't take

very long to bring her child into the world. She, too, then went on to produce twins. The second one arrived as per the book.

"Good old Henry ... all these twins. Masterton down in Hampshire should be pleased with him," Gerald said.

I was tempted to explain about eggs and sperms and fertility, but I was cold and wet and filthy from lying on the mucky straw. I took hold of the rail of the pen and pulled myself stiffly to my feet.

"I hadn't bargained for all this this morning," he said glancing at his watch. "I've got to see someone in the town. Will you be all right from now on?"

"I can probably manage." The sarcasm was wasted on him. He left the barn, brushing straw off himself and dropping the messy towel on the floor. "Who do you have to see?" I called, but he'd gone.

Both ewes had got up, and their lambs were making very wobbly attempts to do the same. I sat down on a straw bale to watch for a while, just in case anyone decided to try for triplets. A wave of exhaustion swept over me, more nervous than physical; I also felt deeply depressed.

The straw bale was warming underneath me, and I sat on, mind uncomfortably blank, and unwilling to face the future. It was peaceful in the barn, the still, damp air was trapping the sweet smell of some of our best hay which the ewes were nibbling, searching out the heads of clover with great enjoyment. I even knew which field that bale had come from.

I didn't want to leave Warren Hanger. I may have been a reluctant cattle breeder, but the safe delivery of all these little woolly people had been very satisfying. The ewes who were still to lamb had the run of the largest space, but those who now had lambs each had a small pen made of hurdles surrounded by draught-proof straw bales. I wanted to build a pen for myself and lie down to sleep surrounded by these contented animals - until the damp smell of amniotic fluids began to rise from my clothes.

I trudged up the hill towards a hot shower and the next phase of my life.

CHAPTER THIRTY SIX

Gerald came back just as I had showered and changed. I should have felt refreshed, but a dull headache was creeping up the back of my head towards its favourite lodging place, over my right eye.

"Well, I've been to see the estate agent," he said. "And he's suggested we put the farm on the market as soon as possible. Apparently things are very quiet at the moment but if it goes up for sale now it may catch the spring-time buyers."

I fetched some aspirins and a glass of water.

"Say something, Jill."

"I don't want to leave."

He sighed.

"Perhaps you'd better go and lie down for a while. Is it a headache? Maybe we should discuss this later."

That evening after dinner, he poured me a large gin and tonic.

"Jill, we have to talk," he said.

"About Hazel?"

He went white.

"I meant about the farm. What do you mean - Hazel?"

"I know about you and Hazel."

I could see he didn't know how much I knew about them, which was a good job as it was really very little, and I could have been quite wrong.

"How do you know?" he said. I wasn't wrong after all.

"It doesn't matter." The aspirins hadn't worked on

my headache and suddenly I didn't have the energy to plead for our marriage. "Do you want a divorce?"

This wasn't going the way he'd expected – I'd taken the wind out of his sails - handed him his future on a plate. I forced my mind to stop thinking in clichés, caused probably by the combination of tiredness and what was proving to be a very strong gin. For some strange reason I wanted to giggle...my world was coming unglued and I wanted to giggle. I choked.

"I, er ... are you laughing? I've never understood you, Jill."

"No." I struggled to control myself - this was no time for hysterics. "Perhaps you haven't. All I know is that somehow we have drifted apart. Maybe living in the country has changed me; anyway, I feel I'm no longer what you want, and to be that I would have to change to something I don't want to be. Hazel might be a better bet."

"Run that past me again; I don't think I quite caught it," he said.

We both smiled, and for a second or two were close again. He re-filled my glass.

"Can we be very civilised about this?" I said, as he handed it to me; it was even larger than the first. "Are you and Hazel serious about each other? If you are, I don't want to struggle to hold on to half a marriage; I'd rather we stopped now. But I don't want to live in London again, and I'll need time to get my life sorted out down here. So can we postpone putting Warren Hanger on the market until we both know where we are going?"

"Of course - you really are being a sport about this, Jill."

I wondered if Hazel was amazingly good in bed; she

was certainly good at being a doting secretary.

"How long have you known about Hazel?" he asked.

"Long enough," I said. "But I don't want to discuss her. I think I'm going to bed; those were very strong gins."

"I'll do the 3am ewe check," he said. "You look tired."

Now he was being kind to me. Now - when it was far too late.

"You can do the midnight one as well; that gin's gone straight to my legs...I'd never make the hill."

Three days later Mr. Masterton came to pick up the sheep, and to make sure they didn't get mixed up I sprayed numbers on the ewes, and corresponding ones on their lambs.

He brought with him a very efficient collie - or it would have been, if any of our sheep had been frightened of it; but they were used to dogs, and only Slit Ear retained some memory of having once been driven by sheep dogs.

He put the dog back in the cab of the lorry to stop it becoming demoralised and we loaded the lambs into a pen over the cab for their own safety. Then Cheap and I led the ewes in. Henry was loaded last in a separate pen at the back, an easy operation as he wasn't going to let all his ewes go without him.

"That's a fine ram," Mr. Masterton had said as he shut the rear gates. "What are you going to do with the wether? Do you want me to take him? I've got a bunch going to market next Wednesday; he looks overdue for the butcher."

"No, he's a pet. He stays with me."

I cuddled Cheap as we watched the lorry drive

away up the hill. The farm was suddenly very silent. "Baa!" he said, and I realised I was going to have to find him a companion of some kind. I put him into the dog paddock next to the house and went indoors.

This was it then...I had no reason for not getting on with trying to find somewhere to live; I wasn't a reluctant farmer any more, I was now a redundant farmer.

Looking through the houses for sale column in the local paper was deeply depressing, I had fallen in love with what was almost the most expensive area of England as far as property prices were concerned. I spent the rest of the day in a strange sort of limbo, starting a job and then moving on to the next before it was finished, even putting up a bag of clothes ready for Oxfam, a sort of token packing.

Late in the afternoon, when I would normally have been feeding the animals, I took the dogs and walked down to the bottom barn. There was the sharp smell of impending frost in the still air and the sun was already fairly low down in the western sky.

The cawing of rooks came faintly from the bottom of the valley, as they made their way back towards the remains of last year's nests of jumbled sticks, in the tall elms behind the church. They shared this general area with a flock of jackdaws, which seemed to prefer the church tower for their roosting place.

The rank smell I had learned to associate with the presence of foxes caught my nostrils, but when I tried to trace its direction, it disappeared.

The three dogs raced ahead of me as we reached the bottom yard, hell-bent on a rat hunt in the straw bales in the barn. I left them to it, and walked across the field to our boundary with the wood. I knew the dogs would be rummaging in the straw until I called them off and didn't want to wait for them in that silent barn, empty now of all the ewes and lambs.

A movement from further up the field revealed a fox moving slowly across the grass towards the little stone bridge over the stream, pausing from time to time to dig up a juicy worm. Reaching the bridge, he sat down and scratched the back of his neck, before marking a tussock of grass by the low stone pillar with his pungent scent, and then trotting across and disappearing into the bushes running along the bank of the stream.

The sun was now a huge red ball, balancing on the top of the Downs, and it was getting chilly. I watched it sink until the last rays, as it slipped out of sight, turned the fluffy cumulus clouds to flaming orange, followed a few minutes later by deep pink.

A short burst of barking from the barn meant that the dogs had actually sighted their quarry. I could picture the rat peering contemptuously down at them from the top of the bales. They had never caught one yet.

There was the fox again. He had stopped on the edge of the field and was listening to the dogs, before trotting into the shadows of the wood, heading in the general direction of Conor's pheasant pens.

One very bright star began to glow in the darkening sky. As the pink clouds faded into grey, my spirits faded with them.

Why had this all gone so horribly wrong… was I to blame? The farm was too quiet. I missed the sheep - I nearly missed the cows. It was as if the heart had gone out of the place when the animals left.

It was almost dark now and the house was just a

black shape halfway up the hill. I realised it wasn't the house which I would miss when we left, but the land. Every hillock, hollow and boggy patch of it was imprinted on my mind.

The moon began to rise above the hill behind the house, a perfect golden moon, rivalling the setting sun in its size, and I pulled the scarf up around the back of my neck. The dogs were quiet again; they would be digging into the rat runs in the earth floor behind the straw bales.

A stick cracked in the wood just behind me and I spun round.

"Christ!" said a deep voice.

"Who's that?" I said, my heart thumping, then began to walk fast across the field towards the barn.

"Jill?" This time I recognised the voice and relaxed; it was Conor. I walked back to the fence.

"Jill? - You startled me, you were standing so still I didn't see you till you turned round."

"Makes a change for me to make you jump," I said. "Good job you didn't have your finger on the trigger." I nodded at the shotgun he was carrying.

"I'm on the lookout for a fox. It took one of my sitting pheasants last night."

I didn't tell him that while he was talking to me it was probably taking another at this very moment. I struggled to find something to say; for the last half-hour I had almost drifted into feeling part of the natural world around me, and suddenly having to observe the human niceties of conversation was hard.

"Is Niamh still staying with you?" I said.

"No, she's gone back to Dublin."

"Do you have any other family over there?"

"Just a son; he's twenty now. My parents are both dead."

"A son? ... No wife?"

"Ex-wife ... we married very young ... it didn't work out. What are you doing lurking down here in the dark?"

"Being miserable ... the sheep went today. I've only got my old wether left. The farm feels awful with no animals on it, and Gerald wants to put the place on the market as soon as possible...and I want to build a little straw hut in the barn over there and never have to leave."

"A straw hut? Hmmm! It's a good job there are no huffing, puffing wolves around here. Do you really have to leave? Can't you just sell off the land?"

"It's more complicated than that." I was glad of the darkness. If he was going to draw my troubles out of me, it was easier to talk in the dark.

"How, more complicated?"

"Oh, you don't want to listen to my problems."

"Maybe I do." He stood the gun against the post and rail fence and climbed over it into the field. There was another burst of barking from the barn.

"They're after the rats," he said.

"It's their favourite occupation. They'll be miserable having to leave here. So will I."

It was getting lighter again as the moon rose, turning the countryside into contrasts of silver and black. Conor, with his back to the moon, was just a black shadow, but I could feel the warmth from him.

"Well ... this is just a thought," he said. "But would it help you two to stay on if I bought part of the farm from you? As I said in the Royal Oak, I am looking for some land, and now I can afford it. Vince, my agent – you've seen him up at the pub, the one with the flashy blue Jaguar – he's just arranged a very good deal on my next book."

"I thought he was something to do with the IRA ... blame Margaret at the shop for putting that idea into my head. What with him and the gun I had jumped to some weird conclusions about you."

He glanced at his shotgun. "The gun?"

"No, not that one, the handgun on your desk ... I'm sorry, I looked through the window when I brought the whisky up."

He laughed. "Oh that, that's just a replica ... it was a bit of research I was doing for the book."

"It's not really money that's the problem, Conor, it's ... well ... " He was standing very close to me, our breath was turning into little puffs of mist in the cold air.

A sudden agonised squawking from the middle of the wood set off all the roosting pheasants into a cacophony of alarm calls. The squawking was cut off as quickly as it had begun.

"That bastard! He's had another one." Conor turned and reached for his gun.

"Don't, please don't kill him." I put my hand on his arm and he turned back to me. Before I could remove my hand, he had covered it with his own and held it there. I began to have difficulty breathing.

"You were going to tell me your troubles...is it Gerald?"

It all came out. Hazel, the impending divorce, my uncertain future.

"Do you still love him?"

"I ... no ... if I'm honest." Couldn't he hear my heart thudding in that still night air? "We seem to have drifted apart over this last year. I think I've changed, but Gerald hasn't. I'm no longer the wife he wants ... I think the wife he wanted was never the real me. I was just trying to be his ideal. It's difficult to explain. You don't want to hear all this."

"On the contrary - it's the best thing I've heard for months. It might mean that I could be in with a chance ... perhaps?" His voice tailed off into uncertainty. "Maybe? ... Maybe I should shut up?"

The transition from abysmal misery to ecstatic heights had been too fast for me. My brain wasn't obeying the urgent messages I was sending to it. Fling yourself into his arms shouting yes, yes, yes, they said. But I remained rooted to the springy turf, unable to move or speak.

"Are you all right ... do you want me to go?"

"No!" I gasped.

He held me then, and time was suspended - until Flicka brought me back to reality by standing up and putting her paws against my leg. In the absence of rat she wanted her supper.

That was six weeks ago.

Now we were once more standing in the same place in the field, but this time we had entered together from the wood, through the new gate that Conor had just built. The field and the bottom yard now belonged to Conor and me. Gerald was happily living in London with Hazel, and friends of the Barrington-Smythes had bought Warren Hanger and stocked it with three horses, and a large obstreperous donkey called Jed Clampitt, who was already in the farrier's black books since he had dumped him, and his tools, out through the stable door onto his bottom in the yard.

The farm was alive again.

Cheap was living in our field with his new companion, a crazy, totally wild, little black shetland ewe. I hope she never gets anything wrong with her because she's impossible to catch and handle, and can jump over any barrier less than six feet high.

I had been scratching Cheap behind the ears, but he wandered away, and Conor suddenly whispered "Look!" I followed his gaze. He was watching a white seagull which was skimming across the ground two fields away. As it came to the dividing fence, it suddenly lifted, and floated up to perch lightly on a fence post. It wasn't a seagull, it was a barn owl. After a moment it took off again, flying silently towards the bottom yard, where, with a sideways tilt of its wings, it sailed through the door into the dark interior of the barn.

Ernie's owls had returned to the farm.